# Praise for *Quantum Body*

"Almost forty years ago, Deepak Chopra launched a revolution in alternative medicine with his book *Quantum Healing*. It was a time when meditation and the concept of a mind-body connection were considered fringe ideas. Today, dozens of years and dozens of books later, that fringe has become mainstream. In *Quantum Body*, Chopra picks up where his earlier book left off to present a plan for a happier and healthier life. Though I do not subscribe to all his theoretical points, his practical advice is as wise and potent as ever."

—Leonard Mlodinow, physicist and bestselling author of
*Stephen Hawking: A Memoir of Friendship and Physics* and
*Emotional: How Feelings Shape Our Thinking*

"Deepak Chopra has taken heat from skeptics like me for his riffs on quantum theory. But I found his latest book, which links the quantum realm to our innate powers of self-healing and spiritual growth, inspiring."

—John Horgan, science journalist and
director of the Stevens Center for Science Writings
at the Stevens Institute of Technology

"*Quantum Body* is a bold and brilliant integration of quantum science and ancient wisdom, providing us with a deep and expansive understanding of our mind-body, how interconnected we are, and implications for our health. Chopra, Tuszynski, and Fertig provide easy and satisfying tips for becoming intimate with our 'quantum body,' allowing us to turn off our autopilot stress mode, and immerse in our presence and the larger reality we are part of."

—Elissa Epel, PhD, professor at UCSF, coauthor of
*New York Times* bestseller *The Telomere Effect: A Revolutionary Approach to Living Younger, Healthier, Longer,* and
author of *The Stress Prescription*

"The crystal-clear words in this original and fearless book makes the case for the mystery of the quantum field's activity in our living realm of quantum biology and its relevance to the human experience and wellness."

—Stephon Alexander, professor of physics at Brown University, former president of the National Society of Black Physicists (NSBP)

"Allied with an emergent cosmology of an essentially living and meaningful Universe, this revelatory and timely book is a profound guide to empower our collective healing and conscious evolution."

—Jude Currivan, PhD, cosmologist, author of *The Cosmic Hologram* and *The Story of Gaia*, and cofounder of WholeWorld-View

"*Quantum Body* brings readers up to date on what the latest science says about quantum biology and its application to medicine."

—Michael Shermer, publisher *Skeptic* magazine, Presidential Fellow at Chapman University, and author of *Heavens on Earth*

"An excellent, reader-friendly book that will leave you feeling inspired."

—Amit Goswami, PhD, quantum physicist and coauthor of *The Quantum Brain, The Quantum Reenchantment of the Reality You Live,* and *Quantum Integrative Medicine*

"Chopra, Tuszynski, and Fertig dispel dichotomous thinking and, through provocative questioning, lead the reader to personalized enlightenment."

—Jeffrey I. Mechanick, MD, professor of medicine at Icahn School of Medicine at Mount Sinai, New York City

'*Quantum Body* is, at the very least, an intriguing work that cannot be cavalierly dismissed. And its relevance to our lives cannot be overestimated.'

—Bernardo Kastrup, PhD, author, philosopher, and
computer scientist; Executive Director,
Essentia Foundation

'Deftly weaves recent discoveries from physics and biology with ancient insights from spirituality to provide practical advice for maintaining a healthy body and a balanced mind.'

—Donald D. Hoffman, PhD,
Professor of Cognitive Sciences,
University of California, Irvine;
author of *The Case Against Reality*

'*Quantum Body* is a rare exposition of truths, a work of deep knowledge, practical steps for life as well as reality in its most encompassing aspect.'

—Menas C. Kafatos, PhD, Fletcher Jones Endowed
Professor of Computational Physics and Director,
Institute for Earth, Computing, Human, and Observing
(ECHO), Chapman University

# Quantum Body

## The New Science of Living a Longer, Healthier, More Vital Life

### Deepak Chopra

Jack Tuszynski
Brian Fertig

**RIDER**

1

Rider, an imprint of Ebury Publishing
20 Vauxhall Bridge Road
London SW1V 2SA

Rider is part of the Penguin Random House group of companies
whose addresses can be found at global.penguinrandomhouse.com

Copyright © 2023 by Deepak Chopra,
Fertig Metabolism, LLC, and Jack Tuszynski Solutions, Inc.

Deepak Chopra, Jack Tuszynski and Brian Fertig have asserted their
right to be identified as the authors of this Work in accordance
with the Copyright, Designs and Patents Act 1988

First published in Great Britain by Rider
First published in the United States of America in 2023
by Harmony Books, an imprint of Random House, a division of
Penguin Random House LLC, New York in 2023.

www.penguin.co.uk

A CIP catalogue record for this book is available from the British Library

*Book design by Andrea Lau*
*Jacket design by Anna Bauer Carr*
*Jacket illustration by oxygen/moment/Getty Images*

Hardback ISBN 9781846047695
Trade Paperback ISBN 9781846047701

Printed and bound in Great Britain by Clays Ltd, Elcograf S.p.A.

The authorised representative in the EEA is Penguin Random House
Ireland, Morrison Chambers, 32 Nassau Street, Dublin D02 YH68

Penguin Random House is committed to a sustainable future
for our business, our readers and our planet. This book is made
from Forest Stewardship Council® certified paper.

# Contents

## PART THREE

# Expand Your Awareness:
# Seven Quantum Breakthroughs

## PART FOUR

# The New Science of Life:
# Quantum Answers to Old Riddles

# Quantum Body

# Preface

*by Deepak Chopra*

This book celebrates the most surprising turn my life took, which happened more than thirty years ago. I had a medical practice in Boston that was hectic to the point of exhaustion. I took up meditation to alleviate the constant wear and tear of my life. It worked, but there was an unexpected side effect. I became a writer. With no background but bountiful enthusiasm, I was enjoying modest success when out of the blue I had a life-changing idea.

It sprang to mind as a visual image, which showed the human body shimmering with light and energy. This wasn't a medically respectable vision. At some level it made sense, however, and after some inner searching, I had a breakthrough. What I saw was the quantum mechanical body. I had a strong bent for science, and I knew that every physical object has its source in the quantum field. This included the human body. Behind the appearance of blood coursing through our veins, the suppleness of skin, and the mysterious electrical storm shattering the silence of the brain, we are quantum creations. Our essence begins as ripples in the quantum field, a fact that is inescapable.

I found it thrilling, and since I had another bent—for out-of-the-box thinking—the prospects of crossing the quantum horizon fascinated me. None of my medical colleagues would have supported me. We're harking back to a time when even the mind-body connection was considered questionable. The term wasn't taught in medical school, where even the medical benefits of meditation were considered a fringe topic.

The product of my medically weird thinking was a book, *Quantum Healing*, which gave me my first boost into being noticed. The book was a success and with success came a mix of positive and negative results. For mainstream doctors, my venture into mind-body medicine was either embarrassing, cocky, or professionally suicidal. Where I gained encouragement was in the meditation and spiritual community, alongside the field of alternative medicine, which was still struggling for acceptance.

Their struggle became mine. Thirty-seven years later, the fringe has moved to the center. Meditation, the mind-body connection, and alternative medicine (which expanded to become integrative, or complementary, medicine) no longer raise eyebrows. New studies are overturning long-held mainstream medical beliefs, and future horizons look bright.

Even so, it seemed like the right time to take a second bite of the apple. The quantum world is alien and strange. Its connection to the human body baffles people. It would be almost impossible to find someone qualified to write about medicine and quantum reality. But, by great good fortune, I found two scientists with exactly those qualifications. Jack Tuszynski, PhD, is a physics professor and Brian Fertig, MD, an endocrinologist and medical-school professor. Together, they have a wealth of insights into a new and exciting field—quantum biology. Their research papers break new ground, bolstering the science that supports the reality of the quantum body.

As often as the phrase *cutting-edge* is used, there are revolutionary implications in quantum biology, because until very recently, a Chinese wall separated the quantum domain from the vastly larger scale of cells and living creatures that biology studies. Bringing the two worlds together stirs me with fascination. This book puts you in the forefront of a revolution that promises to alter everything we know about the human body.

Thirty years ago, I knew that *Quantum Healing* was just

the beginning of the story. It has taken all this time to reveal many findings that were only hinted at until medical science, physics, and biology caught up. In *Quantum Body*, this new knowledge is hot off the presses, you might say, even though science proceeds cautiously when it comes to new breakthroughs. The quantum body is a newborn, but my innovative coauthors and I are certain it is here to stay.

# Meet Your Quantum Body

*As is the human body, so is the cosmic body.*
*As is the human mind, so is the cosmic mind.*

—Ancient Upanishad

Your body isn't what you think it is. Or, to be more precise, your *real* body isn't what you think it is. That's because your real body cannot be seen in the mirror. It doesn't get sick or grow old. It doesn't fit inside the package of flesh and bones that occupies a few cubic feet in time and space. Very little about your real body is talked about in medical textbooks, and when medical students learn anatomy by dissecting the physical body, they never touch your real body, much less peer inside it with their scalpels.

Your real body is a quantum creation. It rises from the same quantum field that created the universe, but in your case, the act of creation is constant and new every second. Your genesis is here and now. This isn't news to your cells. Their connection to the quantum domain is indisputable. Every thought you have requires your brain cells to exchange electrical signals, and electricity is quantum, being part of the electromagnetic field. You are a quantum creation even if you don't realize it, because every cell, not just brain cells, emits a self-generated electric field. If this field goes dark, the cell has died.

Beyond these basic facts, your body's electrical field, sometimes known as the biofield, connects you to some rich and unknown possibilities. The electrical impulses inside your brain aren't random. There's not a crackling storm of microscopic lightning in your brain but an organized process. Somehow, the brain's electrical impulses *know what they are doing*. When you want to have a thought, words appear in your head; you don't hear static or the white noise that random frequencies would generate. To imagine the mystery behind this, think of living in a house where electricity flows through the wiring and decides to operate all your appliances any way it wants to.

That's an impossibility when it comes to household electricity, but as you read this sentence, the words mean something because the biofield flickers with meaningful activity. Now expand the picture. Not just individual cells or clumps of cells, not even whole organs like the heart and brain, but your entire body is held together by meaningful activity. Every cell knows what it is meant to do. It has even been proposed that the biofield is actually an *electrome*, a totality like your genome. Your genome is an encyclopedia of the knowledge contained in all 20,000 to 25,000 genes in the human body. Geneticists are constantly delving into the information coded in human DNA, but it would be impossible to approach your electrome the same way. Genes can be viewed under a microscope. Electrical impulse are invisible ripples or fluctuations in the biofield. Genes are stable—the ones you were born with remain fixed for a lifetime—but electrical impulses are in constant flux. No two seconds of your life so far have contained the same map of activity in your electrome.

This brief sketch indicates that you possess a quantum body already in a single dimension. Much more is happening at the quantum level than electrical signals. There's a psychological dimension to quantum reality that needs to be explored, and a spiritual dimension that brings wonder and insight to the human condition. These dimensions are beautiful, but they will have to wait. For now, we need to understand the basic nature of the quantum body. The illustration below shows the setup in outline form, where physical reality exists above the line and quantum reality below it.

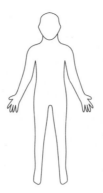

**Physical Body**

---

**Quantum Body**

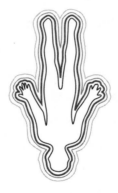

To use the accepted scientific terms, a physicist would refer to the world above the line as the *macroscopic* world, meaning the world of objects bigger than an atom. The quantum world is on the edge of being physical but is much, much smaller than the macroscopic world. The scale is almost unimaginably small.

In the everyday world, your physical body has a definite shape while your quantum body is blurry—it merges into the quantum field, which is infinite in all directions. At the finest level, all physical objects, including your body, dissolve into a haze of energy clouds. At an even finer level, these clouds lose their edges entirely, become shapeless, and vanish as invisible ripples in the quantum field.

Beyond this vanishing act, what is so astonishing is that everyday reality is controlled from the quantum level. Your physical body is like the leaves and twigs of a plant rooted out of sight belowground. If you water the leaves and twigs while ignoring the roots, the plant will die. The analogy holds true for the body as well, which owes its existence to the surge of energy from the quantum world.

Don't be intimidated by the technical word *quantum* and its application in modern physics. It is enough to know one thing: Your true source—the origin of who you are—exists at the finest level of Nature, which is the quantum field. The fact that you occupy time and space is a quantum event. So is the existence of the matter and energy of your physical makeup.

You have been navigating the quantum field all your life, and this journey is all-important. The body you see in the mirror cannot exist outside the quantum field; neither can your thoughts, feelings, or sensations. *If you want to*

*solve the most troubling issues about having a human body,*
*especially disease and aging, the answers lie only at the source.*
The same is true of mental and psychological issues, from
anxiety and depression to Alzheimer's disease. The reason
these mysteries remain unsolved is due to limited vision.
We have failed to look beyond flesh and blood to their
origin.

Expand your vision, and new truths emerge. Here is
the first and most important one: Nothing can happen to
you, for good or ill, until it happens at the quantum level.
A ripple in the quantum field determines whether you feel
pleasure or pain, fall in love, feel hostility, experience an
"aha" moment, or think the same routine thoughts. A cancer cell becomes malignant because of a distortion in its
genetic activity that occurs as a quantum event before any
physical manifestation of disease.

Expanded vision reveals a second truth of the most intimate kind: Your well-being, or the lack of it, depends
entirely on the quantum field. This sounds like a sweeping
generalization. If you feel vibrant and alive, you might explain it any number of ways: You have healthy self-esteem;
your body is fit and healthy; your relationships are loving
and secure. Finances, success at work, and even the weather
contribute their part. But these separate elements have the
same source, the quantum field. And the quantum body is

your portion of the field, the part you call "me" in body, mind, and spirit.

We are offering a revolutionary perspective here, and in the pages that follow we will further explain what the quantum body really is and how to make it a daily reality. But the need for a new model of the human body is urgent. The existing model has run into many unsolved mysteries. Setting aside the ongoing struggle against disease and aging, the simple mechanics of the body are totally inexplicable. Consider some basic facts.

At this moment, your physical body is like a snapshot that exists only for an instant before everything that is you moves on, leaving the picture behind as a discarded image. The you that you see in a selfie no longer exists. Inside every cell, a thousand processes have changed in the time it took you to read this sentence. In the same instant, your brain fired in unpredictable patterns woven within its quadrillion connections. Billions of oxygen molecules entered your bloodstream while billions of molecules of carbon dioxide departed. The simple fact that you shed 20 million skin cells a day points to the transitory nature of life.

The current model of the human body is overwhelmed by such bewildering complexity. At every level—physical, mental, emotional, and beyond—constant change keeps surging forward, and 99.999 percent of this change is occurring automatically. You are either benefiting from change or being damaged by it.

This is the crux of well-being. So much is happening automatically that trying to push things in a positive direction seems impossible, like trying to catch the water from a rainstorm one drop at a time. Even with all the medical advances that revolve around the human genome, the wellness movement remains stuck in the old model. Lifelong well-being has run into serious obstacles, including the following:

- No matter how good your diet is, you have no control over what happens to the food once it enters your digestive tract.
- No matter how positive your thoughts, you have no control over how your thoughts interact with a lifetime of stored memories, which are the relics of your past thoughts.
- No matter how perfectly the human brain is understood, you cannot predict your next desire, wish, fear, insight, or memory. Once any of these impulses arises, it has already vanished before the next impulse appears.

That's barely a thumbnail sketch of why our view of well-being needs to be revolutionized. Consider everything else that modern medicine says you can't control—your immune response, the activity of your genes, the ability of cells to clear out toxins, the teeming microorganisms inside your digestive tract. Each of these areas contains a dozen mysteries, but the real mystery is how you manage to exist as a functioning human being at all.

That's the mystery this book aims to solve. *The essence of who you are, the 99.999 percent outside your conscious control, is totally under control—from the quantum level. Your quantum body holds the master switches to every function inside you.* Here is where you can find your true self. Your true self embraces body and mind as a whole. It isn't a thing with a fixed location—there is no region of the brain that creates the self. To be the real you requires the whole stream of life to course through you.

Because the quantum field is infinite, so is your quantum body. This seems inconceivable if you identify only with your physical body and its many limitations. But the truth emerges if you shift your attention to information. Anything that exists can be reduced to information, like the digital zeros and ones embedded in a computer's operating system. Your bloodstream carries billions of bits of information to every cell, which is impressive but still not infinite.

We get closer to infinity with the immune system. When a white cell runs into invading bacteria or viruses, what really happens is that information confronts information. If the white cell detects that the invader's genetic information matches a known threat, the invader is destroyed. The immune system stores the knowledge of who is friend or foe, going back as far as your ancestral line and even earlier to the rise of hominids and the emergence of mammals. In terms of information, a single cell invisibly encapsulates every immune response for millions of years.

Information is invisible, but, like matter and energy, it cannot be destroyed, only distorted. If you have spring allergies or hay fever, completely innocuous pollen is being misread by your immune system. "I am harmless" is read as "I am a danger," and, based on a wrong message, the allergic response kicks into overdrive. A host of defenses (primarily the histamine response, which triggers a runny nose, red eyes, congestion, and low energy) makes you suffer. The fact that these physical symptoms are based on invisible information is the reality. But where did things go wrong?

We can answer this question by knowing just one thing: Information is perfect at the quantum level. Before it invades your body, a particle of dust or pollen is a clump of chemicals coded with information, none of which is harmful in and of itself, just as the hydrogen and oxygen in a drop of water aren't harmful.

Harmless information goes wrong somewhere along the following pathway.

Quantum Body—> ? —> Physical Body

The question mark stands for a profound mystery. Somehow, somewhere, information that starts out perfectly harmless takes a wrong turn. Why? Through a failure of intelligence. The reason the immune system is often called a "floating brain" is that each white cell contains enormous intelligence. It knows what to do. So, if it does the wrong thing—making you sneeze all day with hay fever or causing a child who is allergic to peanuts to go into anaphylactic shock, which is potentially fatal—this is a failure of intelligence. There is no difference between an immune cell mistaking the identity of a dust particle and you mistaking a face in the crowd for someone you know when the person is actually a complete stranger.

Your quantum body is the central hub for every process that requires intelligence, just as a power plant is the central hub for everything that requires electricity. The prospect of the power grid being brought down by technical failure or sabotage is far more dreadful than the prospect of a toaster or a light bulb burning out. Likewise, the prospect of having your quantum body fail you is far more serious than any single symptom of disease and aging.

We have arrived at the two most powerful conclusions that drive this book.

> Well-being is weakened whenever there is a failure of intelligence.

> Well-being is strengthened when intelligence flows naturally.

When we unpack these two ideas in the following pages, you will be able to revolutionize your state of well-being from the source.

Fortunately, your quantum body knows how to take care of you and can never lose even a scrap of its intelligence. Disease and aging arise further downstream. When someone succumbs to a heart attack or cancer, intelligence has failed in one system (the cardiovascular system in the case of a heart attack) or just a single cell (the malignant cell from which cancer develops). By comparison, this is the tiniest fraction of the intelligence that keeps every cell alive.

Now you are faced with an exciting prospect. *Instead of being anxious about cells, tissues, organs, and systems, which aren't under your control, you can live from the source where all controls are overseen by your quantum body. There, all information is perfect, the flow of intelligence is never wrong or distorted, and the creative possibilities for the future are boundless. Living from your source reveals that the infinite is personal and within reach.*

Living this new reality requires a skill set that we will teach you to master. We will erase the question mark that keeps the quantum body a mystery. By its very nature, the flow of intelligence should be unbroken. Local distortions are fixable, but this is possible only at the level of solutions, not at the level of the problem.

Rest assured that every aspect of well-being is controlled by the quantum body. Your true self awaits you there, holding out secrets beyond the realm of the imagination.

# PART ONE

## Lifelong Well-Being

# How Well-Being Got Stalled

We are all living a paradox that needs to be unraveled. At the level of the quantum body, existence is perfect. A flow of creative intelligence organizes everything without making any mistakes. There is no aging, sickness, or death. The quantum field ripples with vibrant energy that is inexhaustible. The paradox comes about when you shift your gaze to the everyday world, which is rife with imperfection. Aging, sickness, and death befall everyone. The DNA that controls every life process makes mistakes. People live with problems for which they can find no creative or intelligent solutions.

The solution to this paradox has eluded human beings for millennia, but consciousness keeps evolving and, as it evolves, partial solutions have appeared. Well-being involves creative solutions in more than one dimension of life.

*Physical well-being* exists if you are able to live a long life in good health.

*Mental well-being* exists if you retain clear, sharp thinking.

*Psychological well-being* exists if you are happy, of which a major component is being free of anxiety and depression.

*Spiritual well-being* exists if your life has higher purpose and meaning.

There are specialists in all these areas (doctors, psychotherapists, life coaches, ministers, priests, and rabbis), and none of them are physicists. The quantum revolution hasn't reached the complex issue of well-being. A physicist has a right to say, "That's not my job," but the larger issue is that the connection between the quantum field and everyday life hasn't been made.

In the preceding chapter we've made the connection

intellectually. Our aim was to get rid of the question mark in a simple diagram.

Quantum Body—> ?  —> Physical Body

Now you know that creative intelligence removes the question mark. The connection between the quantum body and the physical body is a flow of creative intelligence that sustains everything in existence. The quantum doesn't inhabit a microscopic world totally apart from everyday life. The quantum field lies at the foundation of the world. With this big idea in mind, we need to erase another question mark.

Perfection—> ?  —> Imperfection

If the quantum world runs perfectly at the level of quarks, electrons, atoms, and molecules, what happened to create the imperfections of everyday existence? We can divide the question into the major parts of well-being.

## Physical well-being

The baseline for physical well-being is life span. For centuries this was a gloomy subject (a famous quotation from the English philosopher Thomas Hobbes held that life in the state of nature was "nasty, brutish, and short"). Modern life span has greatly improved on Nature. According to the U.S. Census Bureau, the average American male in 1960 could expect to live 66.6 years; by 2015 this had increased to 77 years. For women the jump went from 73.1 years to 81.7 years.

The COVID-19 pandemic reversed this trend, reducing the average life span from 79 to 77–78 years, but life span as a raw number isn't all that useful. During the pandemic, American health span—the period of life spent in good health without chronic disease or disability—continued to increase. By 2019 the average health span had increased to 66 years. Yet from a different viewpoint that's a very discouraging number. It implies that more than a decade of chronic disease or disability will be endured before a person dies.

In fact, health span faces all kinds of obstacles. The biggest is the gap between white, educated, well-to-do Americans and those who do not have these advantages. Next comes modern medicine, ironically, which can keep chronically ill people alive longer than ever. A dramatic instance is the chance of dying from a stroke. Between 1975 and 2019 deaths from strokes in America declined dramatically. For women, 88 stroke deaths per 100,000 decreased to 31; for men the decrease went from 112 to 39.

Unfortunately, being kept alive after suffering a stroke doesn't mean that your health span has improved. Only 10 percent of people fully recover from a stroke (almost always from a mild stroke). With proper rehabilitation treatment, improvements will show up in more patients than before. Around 25 percent have only minor impairments and 40 percent have moderate impairments that require special care, which can be expensive and difficult for both patients and caregivers.

It is theorized that life span could feasibly reach age ninety-five, and right now the elderly are the fastest-growing sector of the population. This gives rise to a terrible vision of a crippled and demented population of seniors. Already many households find themselves taking care of Alzheimer's patients who have nowhere else to go. One study estimates that taking care of someone with dementia reduces the caregiver's life span by five to eight years.

To put it briefly, the gap between life span and health span is enormous. Physical well-being has run into a dead end. You are trapped in a life-span lottery that determines who will age healthily in a random, unpredictable fashion.

## Mental well-being

The normal state of mental well-being is a clear mind that thinks sharply. What people fear as they age is two great enemies: memory loss and dementia. This is a case where fear has outstripped reality. After age sixty-five, about 40 percent of Americans experience some memory loss, and this is typically minor enough so that everyday life goes on normally. More optimistic research holds that 80 percent of the elderly essentially haven't suffered meaningful memory loss.

Rates of dementia are marginally declining. The good news is that the rates are much lower than one might gather from popular media. The World Health Organization estimates that only 5–8 percent of people over sixty-five live with dementia, and almost three-quarters of those are over seventy-five. American estimates seem to be worse, but these figures are probably due to better measurements. Around 10 percent of Americans over sixty-five live with Alzheimer's.

## Psychological well-being

The perception that we live in troubling times isn't wrong. The Gallup Organization, which has done worldwide polling on how happy people are, found in 2022 that there was more unhappiness, worry, dissatisfaction, and mental struggle than ever before in its research. The lockdown period of the pandemic sharply increased everyone's stress. One result was a rise in divorces and domestic abuse. There were also increases in depression and anxiety, but the rise and fall of those numbers is misleading.

Whether in the best of times or the worst of times, depression and anxiety are at epidemic levels already. There is no cure for either disorder, especially in chronic cases (mild bouts of depression tend to improve on their own). The only recourse, when it comes to mainstream therapeutic options, is to prescribe drugs that alleviate the symptoms. Couch therapy can bring about lasting improvements but is too time-consuming and expensive for any but the most privileged. Literally billions of dollars are being thrown at an insoluble problem just to put a better face on it. In cases of mild to moderate depression, for example, the leading antidepressants struggle to do better than placebos.

Psychology is complex, and one can toss out statistics that don't help the situation. Nearly one in five American adults live with mental illness, but by other estimates more than twice that number have some kind of psychological problem and should seek help. The psychotherapy community says that 75 percent of people who go into therapy receive some benefit, but a somewhat notorious study showed that people on the waiting list to see a psychiatrist improve more than when they actually see one.

Even the baseline for normal happiness is deeply in doubt. The study of human psychology followed a medical model for a long time, meaning that the focus was on sickness and how to relieve it. Only in recent decades has the field of positive psychology emerged, which looks at how to optimize happiness. But there is no consensus except perhaps the gloomy one that happiness is difficult to achieve and temporary once you do achieve it.

People are very bad at predicting what will make them happy in the future. "If I only had X" is unreliable, whether X is a baby, more money, a better job, or the perfect spouse. Even when these objects of desire are attained, people don't experience the boost in happiness that they expected, and sometimes not at all. Being the parent of a newborn baby is one of life's most stressful experiences for the first year. One-third of lottery winners eventually declare bankruptcy and 70 percent go broke. The burden of winning a huge windfall often leads to a diagnosable condition known as Sudden Wealth Syndrome. Its symptoms include depression, paranoia, social isolation, uncertainty, and shock. In the worst cases, the person suffers an identity crisis. The answer to the question "Who am I?" is a shock to the system when you suddenly find yourself rich.

In short, happiness is an age-old mystery that modern life hasn't solved and that modern stress has made worse.

## Reality doesn't bite

It's good to be a realist, and, realistically, the paradox of well-being isn't being solved. Current means barely move the needle, despite medical advances and the gifts of modern technology. Nobody was made happier in a meaningful way by buying the latest iPhone or mega-screen TV. The old strategies that barely worked in the past—getting rich, gaining social prestige, marrying well, attaining a powerful position—had limited success in the past. Repeating the same behavior in the future won't improve their results.

The quantum model offers a solution because it is based on "real" reality, not our wishful thinking and false hopes. The quantum domain is what gives this world its reality. One of the most important sayings gleaned from the Bhagavad-Gita is a declaration by Lord Krishna: "I am the field and the knower of the field." These words are uttered on the eve of a ferocious battle with chariot warriors lined up on both sides. The field of battle will be their whole world when dawn comes.

But Lord Krishna turns the battlefield into the field of life when he says, "I am the field." He means that the divine essence in everyone is the whole of life and that it knows everything. In a remarkable parallel, the same can be said about the quantum field. If we look deeply enough, we discover that we are the quantum field and that everything is known there. In this book we are entirely avoiding mysticism, but a famous medieval theologian had an insight 900 years ago in Germany. Born Johannes Eckhart around 1260 in the feudal region of Thuringia, he became the mystic known as Meister Eckhart.

One of his sayings could have been uttered by someone living in a quantum reality. "God is creating the entire universe, fully and totally in this present now. Everything God creates, He creates now all at once." Translated from a religious perspective, these words aren't mystical. They describe what the quantum field is doing—creating every experience now and all at once. The smallest details conform to the big picture. This is another way of looking at well-being. What if the answer is here and now, all at once?

We believe it is. Connecting to quantum reality takes you away from the level of the problem to the level of the solution. The perfect state of the quantum body should be everyone's starting point. Otherwise, we will continue to restlessly roam from one problem to the next. A pandemic subsides, but a war arises. Economic growth returns, but inflation runs rampant. One can be fixated on bad news for a lifetime.

A better way, a way of escape, is needed. Meister Eckhart offered a clue when he affirmed that "God is closer to me than I am to myself." The primal source is closer to us than the self we identify with. Go to the source, and the true self is there, holding out the possibility of lifelong well-being for the first time.

# The Quantum Solution

I f you take a quantum perspective, the whole problem
of well-being is that it remains stuck at the level of
the problem. One of the fundamental principles we've un-
folded is that the quantum field doesn't age or get sick. It
operates through the flow of creative intelligence, and unless the flow is blocked or distorted in some way, life is always evolving. In personal terms, that means that your
choices will support your evolution in body, mind, and psychology. (Spirit also needs to be included—it will be addressed in Deepak's Epilogue.)

At the level of the solution, things look very different.
We do not confront the *results* of mistakes but the *cause* of
mistakes. By getting at the cause, you can ask the right
questions and take the corrective measures needed before
symptoms appear. You want support from the quantum

body first and foremost. Further down the line, this support turns into the healthy operation of cells, tissues, and organs. The closer you can get to the source, the more powerful your actions will be.

With any aspect of well-being, creative intelligence is the one factor that applies across the board. Let's take a critical issue that should concern everyone; namely, nervous system overload.

The frenetic pace and chronic stress of modern life have overwhelmed the central nervous system, specifically the involuntary or autonomic nervous system. It is responsible for all the processes, from heartbeat to respiration and digestion, that run independently of your conscious actions. But we aren't designed to be robots, everyone intrudes with interventions that affect the involuntary nervous system. At that point, when we do anything consciously, the other side, the voluntary nervous system, kicks in. Creative intelligence governs both.

In the lives of countless people, too much is happening too fast. Automatic responses inherited from our prehistoric ancestors are hurting instead of helping. The default settings in the brain that should return the body to a normal state of balance have proved ineffective. Added together, these distortions of normal functioning have led to a collective overload of the central nervous system.

To gauge where you stand, here are the typical causes of this overload. The list is in no particular order, since each person's lifestyle will have a different profile.

## Why Do You Get Overloaded?

Overwork

Pressures at work

Taking work home

Anxiety and depression

Lack of downtime during the day

Lack of good-quality sleep

Lack of exercise

Constant distractions (texting, video games, round-the-clock news reports)

Family and relationship stresses

Poor-quality diet, overeating

Severe trauma

Physical illness

Excessive noise

All these causes, which may be physical, mental, or psychological, are typical of modern society everywhere. It would be a rare person who didn't recognize several if not many ways in which the nervous system gets overloaded. This doesn't happen all at once. We've learned to accept as normal a daily level of stress, speed, noise, distraction, and pressure that our bodies are ill equipped to manage.

Filtered through creative intelligence, each of these damaging causes weakens the connection with our source, and distortions begin to creep in. What the body wants when any distortion occurs is to return to its normal state of balance, or homeostasis. Unlike a bathroom scale, which returns to zero as soon as you step off it, your body uses dynamic balance. It adjusts to whatever you happen to be doing. If you run a marathon, jog around the park, or saunter through a department store, your body knows the difference and adapts accordingly. Creative intelligence knows how to return to the state of homeostasis even after the most extreme activity.

It doesn't take prolonged, repeated patterns of imbalance to seriously impair homeostasis. A classic study of college athletes in the 1930s had the subjects stay in bed without getting up for two weeks. Over that short period of time, they didn't lose two weeks of muscle strength but two *years*. The cause of this drastic wasting away is known medically as "disuse atrophy" or, in common parlance, if you don't use it, you lose it. Duplicated with modern medical technology, a 2016 study of young adult males had them rest in bed for just a week, at the end of which there was a loss of lean (muscle) body weight of up to three pounds and a decline of as much as 30 percent in insulin sensitivity (insulin sensitivity and insulin resistance are crucial factors in blood-sugar levels connected with diabetes and obesity, among other disorders).

It is remarkable that inactivity damages the body so quickly, but in modern life our extended sedentary lifestyle typically causes the most damaging effects. Prolonged inactivity is a risk factor for coronary artery disease, hypertension, and heart disease. Statistically, it shortens life expectancy, while sitting for long periods leads to structural changes in the blood vessels of the lower extremities.

By the same token, the body quickly responds to small changes that help it to rebalance. Simply having patients who are in a hospital bed stand up for a minute here and there during the day or, if they're able, walk around, prevents the damaging changes of lying prone without any interruption. Your body is so sensitive to gravity that it responds to being upright, even in the absence of actual activity. Gravity is a force that operates at the quantum level, although it has not yet been successfully integrated with quantum mechanics.

There are also metabolic effects of being totally sedentary. As beneficial as regular exercise is, the biggest jump doesn't occur when you decide to take up jogging or running. The biggest jump comes when you decide to get up from the couch. Being upright and moving around is actually a quantum solution. The metabolism in bones and muscles requires us to be aligned with gravity, but there are other quantum processes at work that are just now being discovered.

## Why a quantum solution?

Nervous system overload isn't a clinical disorder. There are no drugs to treat it, although antidepressants and tranquilizers can alleviate some mental symptoms and sleeping pills can alleviate insomnia. But in neither case is improvement guaranteed. What is far more important from a quantum perspective is that the syndrome is so all-encompassing. You'd have to change a wide range of behaviors and lifestyle conditions to really solve the problem.

No one can be on the side of the angels in so many aspects of living. Tackling nervous system overload one element at a time might lead to success in the area being addressed—you might lose weight and stop bringing work home, for instance—but piecemeal changes aren't holistic.

What a quantum approach adds to this picture are two critical insights. First, nervous system overload begins at the quantum level, long before diagnosable symptoms appear. Second, small areas of discomfort, even when confined to a few cells, have dramatic effects on surrounding tissues and organs. Something very tiny can eventually cause damage to the whole body if left unchecked.

We will wait for the scientific section of this book (part four) to describe quantum metabolism and the quantum roots of two major culprits when well-being declines: stress and inflammation. They both point to the need for quantum solutions that embrace the whole of life. Here's a brief sketch of why.

Scientific information about stress has been available for more than half a century, but only recently has it been shown that the greatest damage occurs not from acute stress (a sudden threat to your physical safety) but from everyday, low-level stress that everyone took for granted. A classic experiment with laboratory mice holds serious implications for humans. The mice were given mild electric shocks at random intervals. The shocks in themselves were harmless, but the stress that came from not being able to escape them wasn't. Very quickly the mice showed signs of severe stress and rapid aging. Protracted low-level stress isn't harmless to us, either, if we can't escape it.

The same is true for inflammation. Acute inflammation (from a bleeding wound, broken bone, or burn) is not as threatening as everyday, low-level inflammation, which typically compromises the microbes found in the intestine that support the digestive process (known collectively as the "microbiome"). Terms like *leaky gut* have emerged to describe what happens when toxic by-products from the microbiome enter the bloodstream, setting off inflammatory markers in other parts of the body. Undetected inflammation can act like the spark that burns down a forest.

With this background in mind, nothing could be more urgent than the need for a quantum solution. In the next chapter we offer three techniques that are quantum because they hold the key to a solution that applies to everything in this chapter; namely, restoring the flow of creative intelligence.

# Effortless Practices:
## Breathing, Feeling, Seeing

Every step you take to restore the flow of creative intelligence will increase your well-being. The most powerful steps are much closer than you think. They involve the most natural processes that connect mind and body. When we pointed out that 99.99 percent of bodily functions are outside of your control, we could have phrased it differently: 99.99 percent of bodily functions don't have to be worried about. They happen beyond our notice, at the level of the cell.

But not only there. Some processes are simply overlooked, and it turns out that three of these—breathing, feeling, and seeing—are critical. What they have in common is that you can let them run automatically or you can take control over them. (In terms taught in physiology class, they are controlled by the parasympathetic nervous system, where *parasympathetic* means "semi-voluntary.") Right this moment, the dual control of breathing, feeling, and seeing could be having a profound effect on you. Let's take breathing as our first example, which leads to a practice that is nearly effortless at improving your well-being.

## Whole-Body Breathing

Any symptom of distress, whether physical or mental, will be reflected in your breathing. Breath is a sensitive barometer. Ragged, short breathing is typical of the fight-or-flight response, which is a primitive inheritance from the distant past. But breathing also changes during depression, panic attacks, continued stress, sudden shocks, sexual arousal, and many other states that are subtler, such as being "in the zone," when everything seems to be going right—breathing will be slow, shallow, and at times almost imperceptible if the zone is deep enough.

*Ideal breathing*, also known as yogic breathing, is very slow and relaxed. It is linked to overall relaxation. The body is using oxygen very efficiently (requiring fewer breaths); the mind is relaxed, experiencing fewer thoughts and minimal "noise" from restless, pointless thoughts. When yogic breathing is carried to its ultimate, it is possible to survive in a sealed box buried in the earth for several days. Metabolism is so low under those conditions that the body is in a state of suspended animation.

*Distressed breathing* is rapid and shallow. It barely keeps up with the body's metabolic demands. The cause may be medical, due to damaged or diseased lung function. More often the cause is some kind of stress, either inside the body or from outside circumstances.

*Healing breath* is different from either of these states. It is restorative, allowing the body to return to normal breathing from a distorted state. The healer in this case is the body's own creative intelligence, but, when it is impaired, you become the healer by making the decision to improve your breathing.

Let's pause to investigate just how advanced human breathing actually is—no other creature can consciously heal its breathing. If you are paying no attention to your breathing, it is keeping you alive outside your notice. That you can ignore your respiration is the product of billions of years of evolution. All living things need oxygen, and, in the womb, you passed through the earlier evolutionary stages of life. When you were nothing more than a single fertilized cell, oxygen was absorbed through the cell membrane, the same way amoebas and blue-green algae in a pond did at the primal stages of life. Before an embryo develops lungs, it has gills the same as a fish. At birth you gasped your first breath in the naked atmosphere of Earth, which amphibians learned to do when they emerged from the primal seas.

This whole line of development was invented through creative intelligence, which remembers every step of the way. But the journey didn't end with mammals, even higher mammals like our primate ancestors. The DNA of a mountain gorilla in the mists of upland Uganda is 98 percent identical to human DNA (recent research indicates that chimpanzees are a little closer, at 99 percent). This indicates a biological complexity akin to the human body, but higher primates are trapped on autopilot in many ways that we aren't.

One is breathing. Whatever a gorilla decides to do—walking, sleeping, eating, mating—its respiration will conform to that action. The same mechanism that restores homeostasis is present in all mammals. But our hominid ancestors received an evolutionary gift that is unique. We can breathe the way we want to, including a two-year-old's threat to hold her breath until she turns blue. Sitting in your chair at this moment, you can sigh, pant, hyperventilate, time your breaths, or hold your breath. (The world record for voluntarily holding one's breath is 24 minutes, 37.3 seconds, set by a man in Croatia in 2021.)

Then humans took an evolutionary step that broke through the physical barrier. We discovered the mind-body connection in breathing. This opened the way for the advanced breathing techniques in Yoga (collected in a large area of knowledge called *Pranayama*). It has taken modern medical science a long time to begin to catch up with yogic breathing. The breakthrough came through an unlikely place, the vagus nerve, which is one of ten cranial nerves that branch out from the brain—they are the highways that carry information to and from the rest of the body.

The vagus nerve turned out to be the portal to healing breath, as outlined below.

## Practice #1: Vagal Breathing

A major surprise occurred about a decade ago when it was discovered that a simple breathing technique, known as vagal breathing, is one of the most effective ways to relieve and reverse the stress response. Relief comes in a matter of minutes and benefits the vast majority of people who try vagal breathing.

The method is quite simple: The key is to exhale more slowly than you inhale.

- Sit upright with your attention on your lower ribs and belly.
- Comfortably inhale through your nose until your belly feels full.
- Hold for a count of four.
- Slowly exhale through your nose until your belly feels empty and relaxed.
- Repeat for 5 minutes, making sure that you breathe comfortably without forcing the breath.

(In a simple variant, you can breathe in through your nose and breathe out through your mouth.)

Vagal breathing launched a major new area of investigation known as "polyvagal theory," which promises a wide range of benefits. All these discoveries are based on the nature of the vagus nerve, which is like a wanderer, making its way to many parts of the thorax, including the heart, lungs, and digestive system. The functions it controls stay beneath your normal awareness. Vagal breathing stimulates all the areas that the vagus nerve reaches. We can begin with the heart.

The kind of irregular, ragged breathing that occurs in stressful situations is directly connected to the rapid, staccato heartbeat that is also typical of the stress response. If you have one, you are very likely to have the other. This matters a lot if you want to protect yourself from stress, especially the chronic, low-level stress that is common in modern life. The immediate effect of vagal breathing on your heart is to take it out of a stressed drumbeat rhythm into a more flexible, varied rhythm, which is the sign of a healthy heartbeat. In medical terminology you are restoring heart rate variability (HRV), which turns out to be one of the most important ways to monitor well-being. It is becoming clear that everyone concerned with self-care should consider taking up vagal breathing as part of their normal daily routine.

As a remedy for a chronic stress response, vagal breathing retrains your nervous system to recognize what is normal. In these stressful times, everyone's nervous system bears an extra burden of overload, but, rest assured, the mind-body system always wants to return to a balanced state in all situations. There's much more to say about stress, but this is a good start for everyone, no matter what your stress level happens to be right now.

Polyvagal theory extends across the artificial boundary between mind and body. Vagal breathing stimulates the brain's relaxation response, affecting how you think, feel, and perceive the world. The element of mindfulness enters the picture as you notice when you feel stressed during the day and immediately take a short time-out to practice vagal breathing. Spreading the net wider, the vagus nerve is responsible for 80 percent of the sensory information that comes to the brain, making it the information highway to the skin and the digestive tract. It seems that almost all parts of the body are in touch with each other through the workings of a single nerve.

If all of this seems astonishing in medical terms, from a quantum viewpoint wholeness comes first. Creative intelligence found a pathway, via the vagus

nerve, to keep wholeness in the forefront. This is a
hallmark of the three practices in this chapter.

## Feeling from the Inside: Interoception

The next practice concerns a kind of sixth sense that we
take for granted: how our bodies feel on the inside. Only
recently has the importance of this overlooked sense,
known as interoception, been uncovered (in the West, that
is—Yoga contains many techniques for inner feeling). Your
body is constantly sending signals that stay below your
radar. They indicate that a response is taking place at a
subtle level that usually remains unconscious. There isn't
even a name you can attach to these signals, but if they
become strong enough, a chain of events occurs.

First, you notice that something has changed in your
body, usually in your heart rate, muscle tension, breathing,
or stomach. Second, you use these physical sensations as
triggers to an emotion, which can be positive or negative.
A quickened heartbeat may indicate anxiety, nervousness,
sexual stimulation, or an impulse of love. Third, you identify the emotion, give it a name, and react. The importance
of interoception is that it starts this whole chain of events,

so it functions as the origin of emotions before you know that they are emotions.

Modern medicine is just beginning to explore the implications of this process for well-being. Someone who is insensitive to inner signals from the body might be poor at regulating emotions; this is connected to a higher risk for depression and anxiety. Interoception also determines how comfortable you are in your body and how early you pick up on signs of internal distress. It has long been known that patients often detect cancer before it is diagnosed; they feel a general sense of something wrong without being able to put their finger on it.

Because the brain and the body form a feedback loop, your emotions also change the signals sent by your internal organs. In a classic study at Harvard, volunteers watched a 50-minute film about Mother Teresa and her work with poor children in Calcutta, after which they were given time to reflect on compassion and kindness. The researchers found that one of the most important antibodies in the immune system, s-Ig-A, became elevated during and after the film. The Mother Teresa Effect, as it has been dubbed, lasted for an hour and a half after the viewing was over.

In quantum terms, a single effect—no matter how positive—barely scratches the surface. Interoception detects signals occurring across a field that embraces the whole range of feeling. It opens a portal to "feeling" your way to well-being. The word *feeling* applies to many related responses. We feel emotions. We feel the hostility in a room where an argument has taken place. We feel contented with how our lives are going, or not. Take any area where insight and instinct come into play. How do we access them? Through feeling. Whether you sense danger in the air, fall in love at first sight, get inspired to make a beautiful painting, or experience a divine presence, the word *feeling* applies. The fact is that feeling encompasses the whole of life.

Interoception is pivotal: It functions as a kind of early warning system, rooted in our cells. This points the way to using feeling as a restorative to the flow of creative intelligence in your body. As with breathing, there are three states of feeling.

*Ideal feeling* is marked by sensitivity to everything in and around you. You know and accept your emotions. You easily empathize with other people. Changes in your body are immediately felt, even when they are very subtle. You experience love as naturally as when you were a child. At the subtlest level you sense the presence of bliss.

*Distressed feeling* is highly conflicted. You accept some emotions but suppress others. You are indecisive when it comes to important life choices. You are uncertain about being able to give or receive love, because love is overlaid with experiences from your past of rejection and disappointment. Carried far enough, there is a state of denial that masks the natural rise and fall of emotions. Physically, feeling can get so blocked that your body is numb to all but the strongest sensations of pleasure and pain.

*Healing feeling* is needed to restore all the desensitized or numb areas where distress has blocked the flow of creative intelligence. As with breathing (see page 43), healing takes place at three stages. You begin to notice signals from your body. You perceive that these signals are creating an emotion, and, finally, when you name the emotion, you can accept it and deal with where the emotion is leading you.

The degree of sensitivity that each person has learned to live with varies enormously. At one extreme, a person suffering from claustrophobia will have a panic attack if asked to be in the confined space of an elevator or an fMRI machine. At the other extreme, someone may easily sense their heartbeat and pulse simply by tuning in to them (with a little training, most people can learn to do this, too). Abuse—physical or mental—numbs a person's sensitivity to suffering and makes it possible for them to endure an abusive relationship instead of finding a way out.

We have broadened the concept of interoception while medical research tends to pigeonhole it as a narrow phenomenon. Everything we label as the mind-body connection is occurring at some level of consciousness. The chemical signals that cells emit are markers of creative intelligence. Cells "feel" in their own way as much and as extensively as we do. The argument against this, which holds that only the brain is capable of feeling, runs into the same old problem. Exactly where in the chain of events do organic molecules and atoms of hydrogen, carbon, oxygen, and nitrogen learn to be happy or sad, anxious or depressed? From a quantum perspective, everything detectable on the surface of life was born intact and fully conscious at the quantum level.

## Practice #2: Body Scanning

Any step you take to increase the sensitivity of your interoception will have a healing effect. Your body is a field phenomenon, meaning that it functions first and foremost as a whole, not as a sum of separate parts. Stimulating the field improves well-being, so it would be artificial to single out interoception—if you meditate, practice vagal breathing, do yoga, or improve your sedentary lifestyle, the whole area of inner and outer feeling will be affected.

(A homey analogy is made in the tradition of Yoga: If you pull one leg of a table, the whole table moves.)

The result of improving your interoception is a better interpretation of your body. For example, if you are a runner or work out at the gym, increased heart rate is interpreted as healthy, while if you are sedentary, even a minor sensation of heartbeat might be interpreted as anxiety. Fatigue from lack of good sleep can be enough to start a downward spiral in someone prone to depression, while other people will simply complain of being tired.

The practice we are recommending is called body scanning, a simple procedure you can do in bed before going to sleep or anytime you can lie supine on a soft surface and feel relaxed.

**Basic Body Scan**
- Lie flat on your back, arms at your sides, with your eyes closed. Take a few deep breaths until you feel relaxed.
- Feel the weight of your body grounding you. The sensation is like being pulled downward to connect with the Earth.

- Let your attention freely roam to any sensation. There might be tension, tightness, or discomfort in your muscles, neck, lower back, or stomach, for example. Or there might be the pleasant sensation of heartbeat, breathing, and relaxed muscles. Don't judge. Just feel what you feel.
- Whatever your attention is drawn toward, pause there. Resist the urge to move on or to escape the sensation if it is unpleasant. Take deep, easy breaths, and, as much as you can, let your attention soothe the area. You might visualize warmth seeping into the tissues, or a bath of soothing white light in the area.
- Do not force the process. Your sole aim is simply to feel without becoming tense and wanting to withdraw your attention. Be easy. Stay within your comfort zone. At the same time, pause long enough to let the feeling or sensation register as whatever it is.
- Notice if the sensation causes an emotional reflex, like jitteriness, restlessness, annoyance, impatience, irritability, or anxiety. When you notice such an emotional response, say to yourself, "This is

just another feeling. I don't have to follow it or pay too much attention to it."

- Following the natural path your awareness wants to take, practice this body scan for 5 to 20 minutes, whatever feels comfortable. If you fall asleep at any time during this practice, that's a sign of stress relief and is perfectly natural.

Basic body scanning makes you more comfortable in your body and its sensations. You are helping creative intelligence repair any weaknesses in the feedback loop between body and mind. At the same time, there is a healing effect that can be expanded and extended. Although there is not yet a reliable body of research about interoception and its potential medical benefits, it seems very likely that these would parallel the benefits of meditation, which have been widely documented.

### Expanding your practice

You can expand upon the basic body scan in various ways. Some people make a habit of doing a full scan, from head to toe, every day moving systematically from area to area. The aim is to tune in to whatever is going on at a subtler level. With practice, you can acquire remarkable sensitivity.

Another possibility is to change the signals you perceive. If you detect tightness, for example, you can place your attention on the affected area and set the intention for the tightness to relax. Intention is nonverbal in this case. It isn't the same as willpower or wishing, but more like wanting and trusting that your attention can make a difference, the way a mother soothes a crying child through gentle attention.

If you want to take this sixth sense even further, there are advanced practices in Hatha Yoga and Qigong that rest on the foundation of perfecting body awareness. Many kinds of so-called "energy work" also depend on locating where the stuck energy is located through interoception and then using a specific technique like toning to make the energy disperse.

Those are visions of the possibilities opened by a sense that most people have ignored all their lives, but everything begins with the basic body scan, an effortless and very helpful practice.

## Seeing with Awareness

It might seem strange to say it, but the eye doesn't see. The eye is the instrument for seeing the way a television is the instrument for watching a movie. We would never say that the TV is watching a movie or anything else, but we've gotten into the habit of ascribing sight to the eyes and the pathway that leads via the optic nerve to the brain's visual cortex. The brain doesn't see anything, either, because it takes an observer to see, and without an observer, the brain is blind.

Seeing can be developed to an exquisite degree if you are a conscious observer. Seeing with awareness, in fact, is the secret to higher consciousness. When William Blake rhapsodized that one could "hold Infinity in the palm of your hand and eternity in an hour," he was making a quantum connection. All that is needed is the awareness to see far enough. The unbounded scope of human awareness is everyone's birthright.

Seeing as deeply as you want depends on your state of awareness. We are referring to the many uses of inner seeing, such as seeing what's right and wrong, seeing the beauty in everyday things, seeing the goodness in people, and so on. But when it comes to seeing the way to lifelong well-being, we need to consider the three states that pertain to breathing and feeling.

*Ideal sight* is clear about what is real and what isn't. You see yourself not as an isolated ego-personality, but as your true self, the channel of creative intelligence. You are not misled by irrelevant details and distractions, but you see into the heart of any situation. You aren't blind to human failings, but you see the potential in everyone. Faced with a problem to solve, you see that the answer lies at the level of the solution, not the level of the problem. In a word, ideal sight is insight.

*Distressed sight* is unaware or, at best, partially aware. Reality is viewed through filters. Most of these come from the past in the form of old hurts, bad memories, and setbacks that cloud the current situation. Other filters are the product of self-judgment, wishful thinking, denial, and various distortions that the ego-personality has introduced. At the extreme end of the spectrum, a person can be blinded to the harm being inflicted on others as well as himself.

*Healing sight* brings clarity to clouded vision. (The Vedic analogy is "like blowing dust off a mirror.") Meditation clears a person's inner vision by going below the level of the confused and conflicted mind. There is a quieter, calmer mind that can receive what creative intelligence is imparting. Beginning to have insight is a crucial part of healing. But you also have to start noticing whenever you blindly react according to your default settings without pausing to apply conscious thought.

The mind is set up to use default settings so that you don't have to confront a situation by returning to square one. In fact, your brain is structurally set up with fixed pathways known as its "default network." When you do something passively, like washing the dishes, making hash-brown potatoes as a short-order cook, or making your bed, the default network is working on your behalf. But this default network is working against you if you have the same old reactions to your spouse, your job, or to the prospect of change.

By contrast, conscious thought is active and requires your personal engagement. It's the difference between ordering an omelet and making one; or having a political opinion and writing a cogent political essay. The gap between passively reacting and actively engaging traps many people.

Every adult has amassed enough life experience that default reactions abound. "I like X" and "I don't like Y" cover a multitude of situations. You can coast for a lifetime without actively engaging. In this way creative intelligence isn't simply blocked—it isn't even invited to the party.

Every step you take to increase self-awareness benefits your well-being. Every step you take to remain unaware adversely affects your well-being. Here we need to pause to make a distinction that confuses many people. Being self-aware isn't the same as being self-conscious. If you inadvertently dress in jeans and a T-shirt for a party, only to discover that the party called for formal dress, you are likely to be self-conscious; that is, embarrassed. The fact that all eyes are on you is the mark of being self-conscious.

Self-awareness is expanded awareness of your true nature. It isn't embarrassing and, in fact, has no public face—no one can tell from your behavior whether you are self-aware or not. The confusion between these two states has given *awareness* a bad name. People automatically say, "I don't want to hear it. Don't tell me. Ignorance is bliss," or some version of that. Hiding from reality is excused because a person feels that the truth will be embarrassing, if not frightening, shameful, guilty, or disillusioning.

Here another Vedic saying is apt: Strip away all your illusions, and what remains must be real. Those words are enough to lead to enlightenment if you dedicate yourself to seeing reality as clearly as possible. Far from causing distress, complete clarity reveals that creative intelligence and bliss-consciousness are everywhere.

The practice we are recommending here isn't remotely as challenging as attaining enlightenment, but it rests on the same principle of uncovering reality by clearing your inner sight. Seeing with awareness is effortless once you become used to it, and the benefits accumulate the more you follow the practice.

## Practice #3: Centering Your Vision

The body's ability to return to a balanced state is equaled by the mind's ability to do the same thing. Medical students don't learn about mental homeostasis, but this concept is validated by a range of experiences. Each of us has an emotional set point, for example, that underlies our typical mood. When a severe emotional reaction occurs, as in the grief suffered following the loss of a loved one, we are thrown off our emotional set point, yet typically within six months we have returned to it. Less drastically, mood swings are, by nature, temporary. Happiness and sadness are transient experiences. If they get stuck, then a chronic condition can develop like so-called "morbid grief" or "chronic depression."

Your default mode network (DMN) has saddled you with small and large degrees of stuck-ness. This is revealed by automatic, fixed behaviors and beliefs. All our lives we hear people say, "I'd never do that in a million years" or "She's always that way," without realizing that absolute statements indicate a stuck mind. Absolute opinions block change and shut out creative intelligence. By definition, the next creative opportunity crops up from the unknown. To fear the unknown, oppose new ideas, and insist on "my way or the highway" are blind responses, creating block-ages. Too often we are proud of our blind spots, which makes it seem like a virtue to remain unconscious.

The following practice puts you on the path to clearing your vision and allowing creative intelligence to reach you at the mental and psychological level.

### Return to Your Zero Point

Like the quantum field, your awareness is constantly in flux. In both cases, the field has a zero point, a state of rest from which activity springs. Your awareness experiences the zero point as silent, calm, alert, and pregnant with boundless possibilities. Thanks to the tendency of the mind to return to its zero point between each thought, you have access to your next thought. Silent awareness is the womb from which all thoughts and feelings are born.

Your mind often doesn't take advantage of this natural process. Instead, you revert to your default mode. Therefore, you operate from old conditioning, automatic reactions, stuck beliefs, and the fallback posture of the ego, which is to defend itself from change. Since this all happens unconsciously, you can't return to the zero point unless you intervene and override your default settings.

The practice is simple, taking just a few steps.

- Catch yourself whenever you notice that you are acting out of repetition, habit, or routine.
- Pause and let your automatic reaction fade away.
- Place your attention in the center of your chest.

- Quietly await a new response that fits the situation.
- Act on your new response, but if one doesn't appear, stay centered and exit the situation as soon as this feels appropriate.

The beauty of this practice is that it yields immediate results. Either you are given a new response or you disengage without causing conflict. In either case, you have overridden your default mode. There is also a long-range benefit to this practice. You are training your mind to return to silent mind, rather than its old, accustomed settings. One could say that you are learning more and more to consult your true self, which resides in silence.

Not every situation is equal, naturally. You can spot when to return to your zero point under the following circumstances:

**When do you need your zero point?**
- You are caught up in a discussion that is going nowhere.
- You hear yourself repeating the same old opinion.
- You are distracted and can't pay attention.
- You are sure you're right, no matter what others say.

- You have no tolerance for anyone who disagrees with you.
- You have reached an emotional impasse, where all you can find is familiar anger, resentment, anxiety, hostility, or indifference.
- You feel unappreciated or you find yourself unable to appreciate the other person.
- You feel blind loyalty.
- You feel trapped, suffocated, stymied, or otherwise at a loss.
- You are overwhelmed by stress and pressure.
- You find yourself opposing change simply for the sake of opposing change.
- You are upset or distressed.
- You've reached your breaking point and are on the verge of losing self-control.

Once you notice these situations, which are common in everyone's life, you can return to the balanced state that is your zero point. However, the motivation to change is often lacking. Not only is the force of habit very strong, but everyone feels a desire at the ego level either to win, be right, or belong, depending on your personality type.

You can't expect habits to break on their own or for your ego to give up its lifelong tactics. Only awareness can heal awareness. You suddenly see that there is another way—it just comes to you. At such moments of insight, creative intelligence has connected with you. You can't think or wish your way there; the phenomenon occurs according to its own time schedule.

### Centered meditation

You can pause to await a new response any time you feel the need—the list above outlines the typical situations you might find yourself in. But you also have the choice to get better acquainted with your zero point in meditation. The practice enables you to go deeper and become more settled. Another effect is that you aren't as driven by temporary situations.

Centered meditation is an extension of the basic practice you've just learned.

- Find a quiet place where you can be alone and undisturbed.
- Close your eyes and take a few deep breaths until you feel settled.

- Focus your attention on the area of your heart.
- Breathe naturally, sensing your breath coming from your heart instead of your lungs.
- Don't mind if you get distracted by thoughts and sensations. Gently return your attention to your heart and continue meditating.
- After 5 to 10 minutes, end your meditation by sitting quietly with your eyes closed until you feel ready to rejoin your daily activity.

It is hard to keep up a regular meditation practice—almost everyone is tempted to let it lapse after a while. But you can stick with centered meditation by doing it spontaneously for 5 minutes whenever you feel the need. It's a pleasant experience, and your day is interrupted in the most minimal way.

# A Stress Remedy That Works

S tress is an issue that lends itself to a quantum approach for several reasons. First, stress can't be isolated and treated one symptom at a time. It is a field phenomenon, involving body, mind, personality, and family history. Second, stress begins at a much subtler level than previously thought. Third, the best treatment involves a shift in consciousness, healing the distortions in the flow of creative intelligence where they occur, which is long before medical symptoms of the damage caused by stress begin to appear.

By now you are familiar with this model for healing, which puts you ahead of the vast majority of people—even the experts. As it stands now, stress is an area where the best research doesn't necessarily lead to a better remedy. The best research on stress led to a conclusion that changed the whole complexion of the field. Traditionally, stress had been defined as a sudden, acute response to a situation that triggered the fight-or-flight response. Unless you are involved in extreme situations, such as fighting on the battlefield, being the victim of a crime, or being involved in a major car crash, you aren't likely to need the fight-or-flight response that saved our remote ancestors from predators.

There was a major shift when it was realized that modern life creates not acute stressors but constant chronic stressors. The major finding, which unfortunately gets ignored too often, is that low-level chronic stress is the most harmful kind. The threat posed by chronic stress is a wake-up call for anyone who believes that living in a noisy city, enduring endless traffic jams, working at a high-pressure job, and cutting sleep short are normal conditions of life. You may deceive yourself that this is so, but the evolutionary setup of your body's stress response, which is millions of years old, does not agree.

No one is immune to stress, and despite the claims of some high-powered, competitive people, no one thrives on stress. What, then, can be done about it? Unfortunately, evolution hasn't equipped the human body very well to resist low-level chronic stress, and it often passes without notice, since the symptoms tend to be invisible until a health problem results. Stress-related symptoms begin vaguely with irritability, lethargy, fatigue, and insomnia. If these signs do not cause someone to address the stressors in their life, the next stage is physical, often beginning with headaches, worse insomnia, and digestive upset. Eventually, low-level stress will contribute to serious medical conditions, which will vary with each person. Even at the early stages, responses to stress vary widely and can't be pinned down like the symptoms of a cold or flu.

When it comes to stress, knowledge is power. Once you know that low-level stress is harmful long before medical symptoms appear, you can mount the first line of defense, which is good-quality sleep. Sleep resets the stress response; insomnia keeps it going. Honestly looking at relationships and job conditions that you know are stressful is the second line of defense. Where change is called for, it must be addressed, rather than treated with denial. Others won't take your stress seriously unless you do. Social conditioning has taught all of us to turn our backs on stress as unavoidable or even normal, yet it is neither as far as your body is concerned.

A long-term solution to stress requires knowledge that goes a little deeper. Three factors make stress worse: frequency, unpredictability, and loss of control. Everyone has a range of stress that fits into their comfort zone, psychologically and physically. Some people can take rejection from the opposite sex, which is stressful, and not blink an eye; other people remember their first rejection all their lives. But no matter who you are, repeated stress will overcome your innate resiliency. That is why any soldier, no matter how stalwart or brave, succumbs to battle fatigue or shell shock (aka post-traumatic stress disorder [PTSD]) if they are on the front lines too long.

The stress remedy that works best is to remain within your zone of adaptation. It is okay to go beyond it occasionally, like going on a scary carnival ride or attending a horror movie, where a rush of adrenaline, which is a stress hormone, is brief and occurs under controlled conditions. But repetition, unpredictability, and loss of control are the key factors to address.

Consider the following stress: You must leave your house tomorrow with only one suitcase of possessions and the inability to return for a week. If you're forced to do this by your boss, you would likely be incredibly stressed. But, in a different light, what we have described is going on a weeklong vacation, where you leave home with only a suitcase, or two. The one scenario is stressful because it is out of your control and unplanned; the vacation scenario, while it may be stressful, is much less so because you are in control.

These brief examples give you an index for staying in your zone of adaptation, meaning the amount of stress you can withstand and still return to a normal state of balance.

The indications that you have moved outside your adaptive zone include the following:

- Someone else has control over you in a way that makes you feel unhappy or helpless, such as an overbearing boss. A repeated situation makes you feel lethargic, depressed, and dull.
- The same pressure comes up repeatedly, such as daily deadlines at school or at work. You dread a repeated situation to the point of feeling more than mildly anxious.
- Someone threatens you with a random act of anger, violence, or public criticism.
- You feel overwhelmed, a typical response to working full time while caring for a family and managing a home.
- You feel burdened with balancing your finances.
- You can only deal with something by looking the other way, such as refusing to face drug or alcohol addiction in the family.

This list is necessarily general because people's stress tolerance varies widely. Someone who gets into loud arguments with a spouse may be used to that pattern from childhood and look upon it as a healthy release of emotion, while a second person may feel devastated by those arguments and retreat into silent hurt.

The scientific study of stress has yielded other useful insights. We know that a positive stress (or "eustress") can be just as deleterious as a negative stress. The classic example is that it is just as stressful to win the lottery as to lose a football game. There is only so far that scientific data, however valuable, really helps. Militaries no longer stigmatize soldiers with PTSD now that research shows how prevalent the problem is. But guilt and shame still haunt victims of PTSD, and no consensus exists on how to treat the condition.

Adaptation in the face of day-to-day stress is ultimately psychological. You need to consciously favor the following:

- Feeling relaxed and unpressured
- Enjoying a loving, fulfilling relationship
- Staying in your comfort zone
- Experiencing joy and delight at least once a day
- Learning to be resilient
- Rejecting pressure from other people
- Feeling good about yourself

Conversely, you need to consciously diminish the factors that promote stress, including:

- Putting up with abusive conditions at home or at work
- Submitting to constant job pressures
- Leaving no time for relaxation
- Brushing off the need for good-quality sleep every night
- Enduring constant tension in your relationships or in your career
- Suffering in silence, making yourself a martyr
- Pretending that your happiness does not matter

As you can see, there is enough valuable information here to allow you to heal the stress in your life. Medical research validates how essential stress management is to our health. What needs to change now are socially ingrained attitudes that persuade us to tolerate stress beyond what our bodies and psyches are designed for. Most people still consider stress management a nice idea that never gets taken seriously enough in practice. Adopting a quantum model for well-being needs to reach a critical mass of people. Stress is an important component of the quantum model, yet no one will seriously address it unless they realize that the quantum body exists to bring about all the healing needed at every level of existence.

# Ultimate Well-Being

Well-being is far more desirable than any medical model suggests. You can be physically healthy without the slightest ache or pain. Every medical test can come back negative, and, on the inside, you can feel psychologically untroubled. Yet this state of well-being, which would satisfy the criteria of good prevention, doesn't cross an important threshold. Throw in sound finances, a good job, and a comfortable family life, but they don't cross the threshold, either.

The reason is that your state of well-being, which would be envied by many people on the planet, doesn't really challenge the full scope of creative intelligence. You are like a millionaire content to live on $1,000 because he hasn't been told of his actual wealth. The dream of a Golden Age exists in every culture. Why is it unrealized? Not because our ancestors were so naïve that they clung to myths. The Golden Age exists in consciousness, not in the lost past (or the future, for that matter).

When you go deeper into how creative intelligence operates, the whole picture of well-being is expanded. Ultimate well-being exists, and it is independent of the measures applied to everyday well-being, which are primarily concerned with staying physically healthy and avoiding the risks that threaten a person's health span in the coming years. At the quantum level, the life you should be leading exists; it's only waiting for you to connect with it.

## Being attuned

Going quantum would be meaningless without creative intelligence. If you exclude it, you wind up with blank physical events interacting at random, like shaking beans in a can. Vibrating air molecules, for example, are a blank event. The raucous noise of a city street can be broken down into overlapping waves created by vibrating air molecules. But nobody goes around listening to every random sound on a city street. Unlike a microphone, which has no choice but to register the whole chaotic soundscape, we are attuned to what we want to hear, picking out a friend's voice or the beeping at a crosswalk when the light turns green.

We are selective in what we notice, value, preserve, and cherish. The sight of a starving stray puppy on a TV commercial for animal shelters can stir any response, from compassion and love to indifference, annoyance, or a sudden memory of the first dog you had as a child.

Is it possible to attune yourself only to the experiences that are beneficial to your well-being? When your attunement is perfectly meshed with creative intelligence, you are effortlessly connected to the life you are meant to be living, whereas someone who is out of tune with creative intelligence is fated to be buffeted by the ups and downs of random events.

No one can be totally out of tune—the quantum body gives you perfect attunement at the level of your cells, for example. But mind-made obstacles (known as *vritti* in the system of Yoga) bring about the distortions that cause you to fall out of sync with your ideal life.

## Dharma

At an invisible level, you are flying with a homing beacon to show the way, which is why every cell operates with utmost precision. Even though thousands of processes must be coordinated in trillions of cells, it all happens spontaneously. Your connection to the quantum field defies conception in terms of its intelligence. Your physical body is naturally attuned to a homing beacon that can be trusted to carry every process to its assigned goal.

The Vedic term for this homing beacon is *Dharma*, which derives from the Sanskrit verb meaning "to uphold." There is no equivalent in English, for many reasons. First, the notion of a cosmic intelligence that oversees creation has been ascribed to God in the West, where the religious tradition has been set up as the adversary of science. Second, the fact that Dharma operates invisibly works against it, relegating Dharma to the realm of belief or faith (as the New Testament declares, "Faith is the assurance of what we hope for and the certainty of what we don't see," Hebrews 11:1). Finally, Dharma uses up no energy, occupies no position in spacetime, and releases no measurable data. It is therefore of no use to science, including medical science.

Dharma must be approached as a personal project, whose reality is confirmed in your own awareness. How can you stay on the homing beacon that already supports every cell? A great deal can be learned from the wisdom of the body. Your cells exhibit wisdom in the following ways:

- They *always communicate with each other.* The lines of communication are never closed. No cell resists talking to another cell. If it does stop communicating, something anomalous like cancer must be suspected.
- They *cooperate* for the good of the whole body. Cells don't have egos or feel the need to be isolated or superior.
- Cells *trust* implicitly that they are meant to survive and thrive. They accept without question that Nature will provide whatever is necessary the instant it is required.
- This trust enables cells to *live in the moment* without worrying about the past or anticipating the future.
- Cells view life according to their individual abilities, meaning that *they know who they are.* Despite sharing the same strand of DNA, heart cells know that they are heart cells and not liver or brain cells.
- This knowledge makes *self-acceptance* easy and natural. At the same time, there is no envy or resentment of other cells. For a cell, being yourself is totally fulfilling.

Taken together, these attributes of wisdom in the body describe the possibility of wisdom in the mind. Whenever you find yourself acting in opposition to the life you should be leading, you have drifted away from Dharma. In other words:

- You stop communicating with other people, which makes it difficult to know what you need and what the other person needs. At the extreme, this behavior is self-isolating. You immerse yourself in the negativity of resentment, jealousy, anger, depression, or loneliness, the psychological by-products of isolation.

- You resist cooperating with others, choosing instead to make them your rivals, if you are a competitive type. Or they become a matter of indifference if you are especially egotistical or narcissistic. Typically, however, cooperation ceases because the barrier of "the other" makes other people alien to "my kind."

- You have no trust that you are meant to thrive. Instead, the world is seen as aligned against you. Nature's forces are overwhelmingly powerful in comparison to your weak abilities, and you see threats looming "out there" as a basic assumption.

- You find it impossible to live in the present. Your mind is constantly in motion, keeping you trapped inside a mental bubble. There is no openness to the next instant, and without openness you cannot be present or exist in the now.

- You lose sight of who you really are, being led this way and that by a constant stream of desires, demands, and duties. Since these are dictated for the most part by the ego's need to conform and be socially acceptable, the true self remains hidden.

- You don't feel self-acceptance, because the ego and all the mind-made artifacts that fill the mind lead to a restless sense of self. This self is a wobbly construction, cobbled together from past experiences, and the next strong experience—especially a negative one—will shake your sense of self. One kind of insecurity feeds every other one.

Much can be achieved by applying these two lists, the first one as a guide to a *dharmic life*, the second as a protection against the opposite, an *adharmic life*. Dharma is always aware of you; the homing beacon shines constantly in awareness. In return, you must begin to be aware of Dharma. This isn't difficult, because once you are attuned, your life becomes easier and more fulfilling. The life you are meant to live might seem far away or intermittent, yet the beauty of Dharma is that the opportunity for an ideal life will never abandon you. Nothing is more inspiring.

## Making it personal

So far, the description of Dharma has been couched in general terms, as it applies to everyone. The possibility that Nature already holds out the life you are meant to live is inspiring but not yet specific and personal. But Dharma is nothing if not personal. It doesn't make demands of morality or rules of conduct, nothing external like that.

Dharma is intimate. Its signals arrive from moment to moment, from feeling to feeling, from thought to thought. Attunement must work at the same level. This is in keeping with the psychological axiom that says it is better to feel your way through life than to try to think your way through.

(Note: The small "d" used below designates your individual portion of cosmic Dharma.)

## How to feel that you are in your dharma

You find it easy to remain centered and to return to your center if you notice that you are distracted or stressed.

Stress isn't a constant issue.

You enjoy your work.

Your relationships have a basis in love, which is manifested every day.

You can go inside and connect with a subtle feeling of bliss.

You feel light both physically and mentally.

You are content with who you are at this moment.

Your desires move easily and without struggle to their achievement.

You see a way forward.

You trust that your life is supported by a higher being or intelligence.

You can make time for the most important values in life: love, compassion, empathy, insight, creativity, beauty, truth, and inner growth.

You see the worth in others.

You have a sense of how to go with the flow. You don't put up resistance or insist on being in control.

You don't worry about or dwell on worst-case scenarios.

You know that you are lovable and can love in return.

You are living your truth as you define it.

You aren't tied to the approval or disapproval of others.

You keep your antennae tuned to what is going on inside and outside you.

You are relaxed and open.

You aren't overly bothered by uncertainty, but rather view it as part of arriving at a creative solution.

You see your life overall as creative.

Your spiritual experiences are genuine.

The reason that this list is so long is that the life you are meant to be living is all-embracing. It contains as many dimensions as human experience allows, a range of possibilities that is infinite. Each item isn't meant to be ticked off like a little box. The purpose behind the list is to convey the wide spectrum of feelings—physical, mental, and spiritual in their implications—that are intimate to you when you are attuned to your dharma.

Some of these feelings will arise every day, but not others. Yet if you are successfully feeling your way through life, none will seem alien. The most natural way to live is in your dharma. The greatest gift of self-awareness is that you can prove this to yourself every day by living with love, truth, beauty, and bliss as your goal. Ultimate well-being requires no less.

# PART TWO

Quantum Reality Is Your Reality

# Embracing the Mystery of You

We have invited you to join a revolution in well-being based on a new and better model of the human body—quantum reality. Now it's time to take a deeper dive into this reality, because it is the "real" reality, hidden beneath the surface of day-to-day existence. There are deeper mysteries to solve, and our aim is to bring these mysteries home, to show you that to be fully human, you must embrace the knowledge that the quantum domain reveals. It isn't just the mystery of where the universe came from that requires a quantum answer. You require it as well. You are a mystery that needs quantum answers.

Even though quantum physics focuses on the smallest particles in Nature, these particles exhibit behavior that extends into the everyday world.

The first behavior is *entanglement*. Basically, all the

matter and energy in the quantum field is interconnected. Two subatomic particles that act as pairs can be separated by a distance of millions of light-years, and yet if one particle changes its spin, its partner will instantaneously change its spin, but in the opposite direction, akin to a cosmic dance. In other words, entanglement somehow disobeys the rule that nothing can travel faster than the speed of light. Being connected to the quantum field allows for the organizing power that keeps complex structures from flying apart. Order emerges from chaos.

As applied to everyday life, entanglement is also responsible for order. The organized way your brain produces thoughts out of seemingly random chemical and electrical activity, the precise way that energy is used in every cell, and the ability of your immune system to monitor thousands of potentially dangerous invading microbes are all examples that immediately come to mind. Yet the orderly events forming a chain in your body are innumerable. Everything is entangled with everything else.

The second behavior is *nonlocality*. Nonlocality is how wholeness produces thingness, meaning that the quantum field, although infinite in all directions, gives rise to rippling activity, or waves, that morph into particles. This is the basic act of creation in the cosmos, and in your body. Even though Nature presents itself as separate things from

the smallest to the largest—quarks, electrons, water molecules, microbes, plants, animals, planets, galaxies, and
beyond—nothing is purely a local event. Go deeper, and
nonlocality rules. The smallest mirrors the largest.

Nonlocality is exhibited in your body by the way that
each cell works to preserve the whole. By cooperating and
communicating with one another, each cell has two
missions—first, to survive and thrive on its own; second, to
promote the well-being of the entire body. Immune cells
that engulf an invading virus to destroy it commit suicide
at the same time. Every cell has a fail-safe switch inside to
monitor against mistakes, and, if a mistake occurs, it is either repaired or the cell voluntarily dies. In the brain, individual thoughts rise and fall, yet the brain oversees the
whole process of thought itself, regardless of what single
thought you might be having. In all these examples, nonlocality asserts the primacy of the whole over the parts.

The third behavior is the ***transformation of quanta to
qualia***. *Qualia* is Latin for "quality," which, broadly translated, means the traits that anything displays. The sun is
hot, interstellar space is cold, water is liquid, granite is solid.
These qualia emerge from the quantum field, even though
the field, and the elementary particles it produces, give no
indication as to why this should be so. The same quarks,
electrons, protons, etc., are found in the sun, floating in

interstellar space, or making up water and granite. A transformation occurs between the quantum world and the everyday world. (In physics the typical term in use is *emergent property*.)

Thanks to the appearance, as if by magic, of qualia, the five senses evolved to detect them. Sight, hearing, touch, taste, and smell are qualia detectors. The brain is the central location where the five senses originate, and here a three-pound lump of squishy matter produces the world in 3-D with colors and light, even though the brain consists of gray and white matter. Noise and music emerge from the brain's total silence. Further, beyond the five senses, thoughts like fear, wishing, intuiting, and reasoning are also bound up in qualia. Without qualia, you would have no experiences at all.

And yet, we must be careful. The brain isn't the origin of the transformation from quanta to qualia. Using the principle of nonlocality, it is the quantum field that creates transformation. The brain is just a localized event. In itself, it is made of both quanta and qualia. So is everything in creation. Any object, including your body, can be defined as quanta or as qualia. It took centuries for science to advance far enough to detect the quantum field, yet life itself, going back billions of years, has always been involved in this relationship, because life is organized by experiences. A microorganism in Earth's primal seas will respond to light by moving toward it. At its own level, the microorganism is having an experience. Therefore, existence can be said to depend on qualia just as much, if not more, than it depends on quanta.

There are many more strange behaviors that the quantum world produces, but these three are vital to the quantum body. To summarize:

*Entanglement* produces all connections.

*Nonlocality* makes the whole primary over the parts.

The *transformation of quanta to qualia* creates all experiences.

These three principles are the crucial ways that the mystery of the quantum world works for you. Indeed, your very existence depends on them.

Making your way into the quantum world requires some radical shifts in how you see yourself. There is a famous quote about how hard it is to explain this level of reality, from the quantum pioneer Werner Heisenberg: "Not only is the Universe stranger than we think, it is stranger than we can think." What takes reality beyond the range of thought is the quantum, because its behavior makes no sense in our normal sensory world of solid, reliable objects. Since the same strangeness applies to your quantum body, look at the chart below and imagine that it applies to you.

**Why the Quantum World Is Stranger Than Strange**

- The quantum field causes everything to happen, but itself has no cause.
- Matter is built from quanta, but a quantum isn't material.
- Anything you can see is invisible at its root, which is the quantum.
- Before you can locate a quantum, it hovers in a cloud of possible locations.
- Two subatomic particles, separated in space, even by millions of light-years, communicate instantly, which implies that they "talk" to each other faster than the speed of light. This defies all known explanations.
- Quantum events can move either forward or backward in time.

As strange as these characteristics look, the very strangest is this: Cross the quantum threshold, and space, time, matter, and energy vanish.

It is completely understandable if you can't identify with the quantum world personally. At first glance, there seems to be nothing human to identify with. Yet the strangeness of the quantum world lies much closer than you think. In fact, it is not the least but the most human world—without it, you wouldn't even be human. You'd be a robotic machine. In fact, without realizing it, that's the prevailing model your doctor learned in medical school. Everything at the disposal of modern medicine—every test, drug, therapy, and surgical procedure—is based on the notion of repairing a machine. Doctors, at bottom, are mechanics. To reinforce the superiority of the quantum model, let's tear down the fallacy of body-as-machine once and for all.

## Debunking the body-as-machine

Your body isn't a machine, or even close to one. You have accepted a familiar concept that is riddled with flaws, as the following list shows:

**Why Your Body Isn't a Machine**

Machines aren't alive.

Exercise doesn't make machines stronger—it wears them out.

Machines can't think, wish, feel, dream, or imagine. They cannot experience anything, in fact.

Machines can't feel emotions.

They cannot gestate baby machines and give birth to them.

They can't heal their broken parts.

Machines don't spontaneously evolve.

None of these things are subject to dispute, and yet we passively accept that the body is a living machine, and a miraculous one at that. But if we go down the list, you will realize that the concept of body-as-machine has deprived you of your essential humanity.

*Machines aren't alive.* This fact seems too obvious to state—even a small child knows that she is pretending to treat a baby doll as if it were a real baby. But if that doll is made of plastic, the most essential atom in living things— carbon—goes into it. Around the carbon atoms will be grouped hydrogen and oxygen atoms, which are also es- sential to life's building blocks—organic chemicals.

Once you reduce the human body to its basic chemicals, there is no reason not to call it a machine. How organic chemicals spring to life remains a mystery, as every biologist and geneticist freely concedes. Yet the search to explain life as some kind of magical chemistry trick continues. A wrong assumption leads inevitably to wrong conclusions.

*Exercise doesn't make machines stronger—it wears them out.* If you put a toy on the shelf and never use it, it won't suffer from wear and tear. But the opposite is true of your body—it is subject to what medicine calls "disuse atrophy." Without exercise, muscle and bone shrink and grow weaker. We resist wear and tear by using our bodies. No machine, no matter how sophisticated, works the same way.

*Machines can't think, wish, dream, or imagine. They cannot experience anything, in fact.* This is an unbridgeable gap between us and machines. We depart from our genetic hardware to dream, wish, and imagine. The most advanced computer can imitate but never experience these states. A computer is ultimately the puppet of its programming.

*Machines can't feel emotions.* Computers are based on digital codes, and codes are designed to be logical and rational. Not only are emotions excluded, they are totally undesirable. A computer that told you it was too much in love to come to work today would be a failure. A human being who cannot love might well be called a worse failure.

*Machines cannot gestate baby machines and give birth to them.* This point might seem irrelevant, since factories exist to make new machines. But the mystery of life is involved here. There is no technology that would enable a robot to create itself out of basic chemicals. Your body, and all living things, produces new life spontaneously. The creative spark is elusive, yet we all embody it.

*Machines can't heal their broken parts.* A self-repairing car would put garage mechanics out of business. The opposite is true of your body, which requires the healing response to remain alive—without it, a paper cut would cause you to bleed to death. Cells know how to repair their internal mistakes, and if repair is impossible, they willingly destroy themselves. Healing remains a huge mystery, but it is one of those things we embody without knowing how.

*Machines don't spontaneously evolve.* A machine cannot invent its own new model. In fact, becoming obsolete is every machine's inevitable fate. The same would doom a fertilized cell in the womb. It must evolve into an embryo, a fetus, and a full-blown baby. This ability to spontaneously evolve is true of all living things beyond one-celled organisms, and even they, in the form of bacteria and viruses, must evolve to get past the body's immune defenses. If last year's cold was the only one in existence, it would also be the last one.

If you stand back, you'll see that everything miraculous about the human body stems from the fact that it isn't a machine. A computer might be programmed to worry about its weight or express a sexual urge or feel a pang of nostalgia. But no machine has ever felt what such experiences are like or had any experience at all. You, on the other hand, are the product of your experiences. If you could catalog every experience you've ever had (which is impossible, of course), not a single one is due to being a machine. The notion of body-as-machine deserves to be swept away.

That's a lot to ask, particularly under the current circumstances, where the quantum world is considered enigmatic and strange, beyond the reach of thought. There are many reasons that the quantum revolution never acquired a human face. A shift of perspective is urgently needed. Once you make the shift, however, you will cross the quantum threshold, and then you will know what the essence of being human really is.

# The Cause of Absolutely Everything

Nothing exists without a source, or a starting point, and finding the source of everything in the universe produced the quantum revolution in physics. Yet the quantum world yielded a flummoxing conclusion that many found too incredible to believe. This conclusion was tersely stated by Werner Heisenberg: "The atoms or elementary particles themselves are not real; they form a world of potentialities or possibilities rather than one of things or facts."

If atoms and elementary particles aren't real, how did we—and all physical objects—become real? It is just as easy to trace your brain, heart, and liver back to their quantum source, where they vanish, as it is to trace a lump of uranium ore or a molecule of water. Answering the vexing issue of the "real" reality proved too elusive, so physics was forced to erect a metaphorical Chinese wall that divides the quantum realm from the physical world. If you and I and everyone else agree to live on our side of the wall, we are also agreeing to have nothing to do with quantum reality. Kipling's lines, "Oh, East is East, and West is West, and never the twain shall meet," is a Victorian relic that history outmoded. Physicists are bothered that the two halves of reality don't meet, because logically there must be only one reality.

Likewise, only by including the quantum body can we know what the whole human body is, not just the part we can see. Here we must follow a different track than science. In their search for the ultimate source, the ancient Vedic *rishis* (seers) in India didn't start "out there" with physical objects the way the ancient Greeks did when they first posited the existence of the atom. The rishis started "in here" instead, with the thing that makes us human—conscious experience.

The names of the greatest seers, such as Patanjali and Vasishtha, have been passed down and can be found on the title page of famous treatises on Yoga. In the West the connotation of *Yoga* is spiritual, and the implication is that these are religious tracts. But it is more fruitful to consider the rishis as Einsteins of consciousness because they set out to find the ground state of reality, exactly as Einstein and the other pioneers of modern physics did. Nor are the two tracks—physics and consciousness—as separate as they might appear. Consider what three Nobel laureate physicists have said.

Consciousness is the phenomenon whereby the universe's very existence is known. —*Sir Roger Penrose*

I regard consciousness as fundamental. I regard matter as derivative from consciousness. We cannot get behind consciousness. Everything that we talk about, everything that we regard as existing, postulates consciousness. —*Max Planck*

The Universe begins to look more like a great thought than like a great machine. Mind no longer appears to be an accidental intruder into the realm of matter . . . We ought rather to hail it as the creator and governor of the realm of matter. —*Sir James Jeans*

These are impressive statements from icons of science, serving to merge everything that happens "in here" with everything our senses perceive "out there." Some of the most illustrious quantum pioneers became convinced that consciousness was fundamental in creation.

But modern physics didn't suddenly take off down the same path as the Vedic rishis: The lure of materialism was too great. A universe of "things" existed to be explained in a line going back to Isaac Newton. And one hugely important figure, Albert Einstein, held out against consciousness by focusing entirely on physical reality. (What he actually felt privately is another matter, since Einstein expressed his belief that no great scientific discovery could be made without a sense of wonder, and wonder is a trait in consciousness, not matter.)

## Two paths merge

Through their explorations "in here," the Vedic rishis arrived at a level of Nature that was at the root of absolutely everything, which they named *Karana Sharir*, or "the causal body" in Sanskrit. The causal body is on the far horizon of what the human mind can know. Beyond it lies a domain that is inconceivable, because it precedes space, time, matter, and energy.

The very cusp of existence is where our origin story

begins. The mystic Persian poet Rumi put it more elo-
quently: "We come spinning out of nothingness, scattering
stars like dust."

If asked where they came from, no one would choose
nothingness. Traditionally, they'd choose God; medically,
they'd choose a single fertilized ovum. In times of trouble
the devout don't pray for comfort to the *vacuum state*,
which is the physics term for "nothingness." (In recent decades, there has been a drastic decline in organized religion
in every developed Western society, but the need for God
persists, even if there is confusion about who or what God
might be in the modern world.)

Science isn't solace. Research isn't revelation, much less
redemption. What has awakened today's spiritual yearning
is the dead end our worldview reached, not in the flameout
of "God is dead" but in something more hidden—our belief that existence can be explained without consciousness.
We must pick up the fallen baton passed on by the quantum pioneers, who often had very evolved views of spirituality.

If you know where everything comes from, you know
where God might be found. This is expressed with heartfelt conviction by the modern physicist Freeman Dyson,
contemplating the potential of the human mind.

I do not make any clear distinction between mind and God. God is what mind becomes when it has passed beyond the scale of our comprehension. God may be considered to be either a world soul or a collection of world souls. We are the chief inlets of God on this planet at the present stage in his development. We may later grow with him as he grows, *or we may be left behind.*

Being left behind would be a terrible fate, and to keep up with God, we must evolve. This is the essence of Dyson's declaration. It is a tremendous step to merge Karana Sharir, the causal body, with the quantum body. It gives everyone a new origin story that will satisfy science and our inner spiritual yearning.

But, for you, everyday existence cannot evolve unless the quantum body convinces you personally. We are asking you to change your beliefs; therefore, let's pause so that you can clarify what you believe now.

## Personal Quiz: What Do You Believe?

Using a separate sheet of paper if you want, check your level of belief in the following statements, rating them as **Strongly Agree, Somewhat Agree, Somewhat Disagree,** or **Strongly Disagree.**

1. I can accept that God might not exist.
   ___ Strongly Agree          ___ Somewhat Agree
   ___ Somewhat Disagree    ___ Strongly Disagree

2. Being rational is the best approach to living one's life.
   ___ Strongly Agree          ___ Somewhat Agree
   ___ Somewhat Disagree    ___ Strongly Disagree

3. Spiritual experiences are real and valuable.
   ___ Strongly Agree          ___ Somewhat Agree
   ___ Somewhat Disagree    ___ Strongly Disagree

4. A peak experience or a major "aha" moment can be life-changing.
   ___ Strongly Agree          ___ Somewhat Agree
   ___ Somewhat Disagree    ___ Strongly Disagree

5. Being comfortable with change is highly beneficial.

___ Strongly Agree      ___ Somewhat Agree

___ Somewhat Disagree      ___ Strongly Disagree

6. I believe that love is fundamental in creation.

___ Strongly Agree      ___ Somewhat Agree

___ Somewhat Disagree      ___ Strongly Disagree

7. *Follow your bliss* is advice worth following.

___ Strongly Agree      ___ Somewhat Agree

___ Somewhat Disagree      ___ Strongly Disagree

8. Paranormal abilities are definitely real.

___ Strongly Agree      ___ Somewhat Agree

___ Somewhat Disagree      ___ Strongly Disagree

9. I can accept that prayer works.

___ Strongly Agree      ___ Somewhat Agree

___ Somewhat Disagree      ___ Strongly Disagree

10. Higher states of consciousness and enlightenment are real.

___ Strongly Agree      ___ Somewhat Agree

___ Somewhat Disagree      ___ Strongly Disagree

11. I have personally experienced phenomena I can't rationally explain.
___ Strongly Agree     ___ Somewhat Agree
___ Somewhat Disagree     ___ Strongly Disagree

12. Human beings are still evolving.
___ Strongly Agree     ___ Somewhat Agree
___ Somewhat Disagree     ___ Strongly Disagree

**Assessing your answers**

There are no wrong answers to any of these questions, yet they offer a good profile of your personal beliefs. Most people's answers would tend toward "Somewhat Agree" or "Somewhat Disagree," which reflects the general state of confusion that pervades modern society. The weakening of traditional values has led to a kind of limbo where belief coexists with uncertainty.

However, a strong countertrend, roughly lumped into New Age beliefs, has affected nearly a third of Americans by one estimate. If your answers tend toward "Strongly Agree," you probably identify with this group, for whom the paranormal, for example, is totally possible. You are sympathetic to a new paradigm that would improve society and lead to higher evolution for humanity. But, at the same time, you might also agree that rationality is a good guide to one's personal life, because you are not sympathetic with religious dogma or unproven faith.

If your answers tend toward "Strongly Disagree," you most likely identify with materialism and mainstream science. You might strongly agree, however, that rationality is the best guide to life, because you have a strong skeptical streak. "Prove it" for you is a high bar. Others might see you as stubborn and rigid in your belief system, but this is certainly not how you see yourself.

You are taking a huge step forward if you are beginning to see yourself connected to quantum reality. Getting past the blind spot that besets many scientists—the blind spot that cannot see how important consciousness is in the scheme of creation—also puts you ahead of the vast majority of people, too. The path to quantum reality lies entirely in consciousness. Accept this one fact, and everything we have to say will fall easily into place.

# The Flow of Life

There are two ways to search for the origin of life. One way focuses on the past, the other on the here and now. The past contains the relics of microbes, the tiniest specks embedded in ancient rocks, which are the first footprints of life, although, of course, they are no longer alive. Yet life is constantly flowing from its source right now. You are connected to the origin of life at every second. If you weren't, no amount of nutrients, water, and oxygen—the basic materials by which a cell survives—would do any good. They would lie around uselessly in rivers, seas, soil, and the atmosphere, randomly jostling each other without the slightest evidence of life.

In the journey from your quantum body to your physical body, something miraculous happens. The lifeless "stuff" that lies around becomes creative. It exhibits consciousness. It starts to make intelligent decisions. To a neuroscientist, these traits don't exist without the human brain, but looking to the brain as the source of creativity, consciousness, and intelligence is vastly misleading. The best evidence is that all these traits belong to life itself, and they can be very advanced in creatures long looked down upon.

Among the so-called bird-brained, a colony of crows on an Indonesian island has learned how to use pointed sticks to dig grubs out from their hiding places under the bark of trees. This is considered an extraordinary feat, because crows have tiny brains, and yet these crows have made a conceptual leap. They looked at pointed twigs and saw their potential to be used as tools. The same conceptual leap occurred to prehistoric hominids when they began to chip shards of flint to make the first knives and scraping tools. Accordingly, the same discovery among crows bothers many biologists, but, in reality, a common crow can open intricate locks to get at a food reward, and if the pieces of the lock are altered, it can figure out the new solution for unlocking them on the first try.

On the other hand, dogs and cats fail miserably at opening even a simple latch to get at a food reward. Yet each creature possesses its own unique concoction of creativity, consciousness, and intelligence. A dog recognizes its master, shows affection, obeys intricate commands, and if she happens to be an extremely talented border collie named Chaser, learns a vocabulary far in excess of small children. The vocabulary of young children is 10 to 50 words at 18 months, 300 words at two years, and 450 words at two and a half years. Chaser, who lived to fifteen before she passed away in South Carolina in 2019, was taught 1,000 words by her human companion, Professor John W. Pilley.

Your vocabulary when you were a child exploded beginning at age two, growing from 300 to 1,000 words by age three. Chaser took her whole life to learn to identify 1,000 different toys by name—Pilley accumulated this mountain of toys and assigned a unique name to each one. But numbers don't get at the heart of the matter. For a dog to acquire a vocabulary, the canine must be creative to make the leap to human language. She must be conscious to process what she hears, and she must be intelligent to remember and apply her vocabulary. Border collies are the champion vocabulary builders, but at least a few have taken another creative step. They can look at a picture of a toy and fetch the toy from another room without hearing a word.

## Creative intelligence

There is no adequate model in biology or animal behavior to explain such a leap of creativity, consciousness, and intelligence. For that matter, these traits have no explanation in humans, either. We just take them for granted. Let's use a simple term, *creative intelligence*, to describe such an essential part of life. (The term was already introduced in part one as a critical aspect of well-being.) The flow of creative intelligence is one of the most pleasurable experiences anyone can have. You have already had glimpses of it whenever you do anything creative.

In a creative moment, whatever it is, you feel relaxed and open. Your focus is fixed on whatever you're doing—cooking, knitting, painting, playing Mozart on the piano—without being distracted. There's a sense of freedom and contentment. This state, which is also present in deep meditation, can be correlated with alpha-wave activity in the brain. Yet any such clues are very elusive, particularly when it comes to exceptional creativity.

Einstein's theory of relativity is considered by many to be the greatest scientific breakthrough of all time by a single mind. At Einstein's death in 1955, a local pathologist in Princeton, New Jersey, removed Einstein's brain, dissected it, and sent photographs of each dissected part to be studied. (The remaining brain was donated to a museum at Princeton University in 1998.) Anatomists were naturally curious to discover what the brain of a supreme genius looked like, but the first complete analysis of the photographs didn't occur until 1999, when it was reported, according to a summary online, that "Einstein's parietal lobes—which are implicated in mathematical, visual, and spatial cognition—were 15 percent wider than normal parietal lobes." Even if you believe that such a small difference can account for the difference between a genius and the average person, where in Einstein's brain tissue is the General Theory of Relativity residing, or where did it ever reside? There is also the matter of other people with oversized parietal lobes who didn't change the world through their brilliant insights.

## Living in *chit akash*

But the mystery goes much deeper. Soon after Einstein's theory of relativity rocked science to its foundations, a physicist named Hermann Minkowski made a prophetic pronouncement: "Henceforth space by itself, and time by itself, are doomed to fade away." That was in 1908, but we are still walking around in the roomy space that is everywhere and glancing at our watches to know what time it is. You might compare the situation to somebody who insists on living in his house after it has been blown up and carted away. Take away time and space, and everyday reality no longer exists. Neither does creative intelligence, which, after all, is part of everyday reality.

The Vedic rishis described another kind of space, where creative intelligence flows freely and is always accessible. They called it *chit akash* in Sanskrit, which roughly translates as "mind space." What is meant, however, is the infinite range of consciousness. To the rishis, the causal body is located in chit akash, and so is the quantum body, even though physics hasn't gotten that far yet. It can't recognize "mind space" until consciousness is permitted to be a respectable subject for physics to address.

Chit akash gives creative intelligence a home. It stands behind the curtain of everyday reality like an invisible choreographer who tells the dancers what to do, even though he never appears onstage. Once you see the advantage of living in chit akash, the everyday world loses its seductive charm. Everything good about your life is better there.

We can give many reasons for this, but they come down to one: Chit akash is where every creative possibility begins to blossom. No matter what process you examine, from a single heartbeat to the entire brain, creative intelligence must spring into action. To do that, an impulse arises in chit akash, and it accumulates enough energy to create a physical action you can see, feel, and measure.

The same is true of mental activity. You dip into chit akash to find your next thought. But the word *mental* falls short, because when DNA divides or a strand of heart muscle twitches, intelligence is at work. This intelligence is unspoken and silent, yet infinitely creative. Expand the picture, and all of Nature is intelligent, because nothing can happen in the cosmos without passing through chit akash.

You have been hit with some new terminology, but this is secondary. The primary thing—the thing that will make you want to explore chit akash—is that you can enhance the flow of creative intelligence. This flow moves in, around, and through you right now. Wherever it goes, there is a creative choice to be made. In the physical world, you can flick a switch and the lights come on. In chit akash you flick a switch in consciousness, and much more happens.

## The Gifts of Chit Akash

Wisdom

Organizing power

Dynamic energy

Infinite flexibility

Intention

A clear path to reach any goal

The fulfillment of desire

The ability to correct mistakes

Healing power

Everything listed above is real. If it weren't, the infant universe would never have emerged from quantum soup and superheated plasma. Closer to home, you would still be a single fertilized egg in your mother's womb. Let's follow the flow of creative intelligence from there. A single cell risks its comfortable existence by dividing in two, a process that tears the cell apart, starting with its DNA. But a fertilized egg has the wisdom to take this perilous journey and the genetic knowledge to carry it out. The manager of energy inside a cell, known as "mitochondria," supplies the energy for cell division. The swirling soup of proteins and enzymes is organized to be sufficient for two infant cells. As molecular machines start unstitching the double helix of DNA, an intention is under way, and there's a clear path to the finish line. Any incipient mistakes along the way are corrected to a microscopic degree of accuracy, and by creating two strands of DNA from one, the split in half is healed. You might need convincing that all of this is evidence of creative intelligence, but your cells are convinced already.

The only proof that really convinces anyone is personal. Pause for a moment and choose something you are good at creating, whether it's a delicious dish you invented, a piece of woodworking, your creative writing or painting—anything will do that you get truly absorbed in.

Then unveil its essence by going through the gifts from chit akash to see how they apply (not necessarily all of them). Once you have a creative outlet in mind, ask yourself the following:

How does *wisdom* enter in, meaning the accumulation of skill and knowledge?

How *organized* and *efficient* are your actions as you create?

Do you *gain energy* from it?

Do you enjoy being *flexible* and *spontaneous* as you create?

When you set out with an *intention,* does it unfold easily and enjoyably?

Does your creativity make you feel *fulfilled*?

Are you good at learning from your *mistakes*?

Is there a sense of *healing* and *wholeness* in your creativity?

If you are fortunate enough to feel inspired by what you do, at the level of chit akash all these elements click into place. You are a creator, and you are taking part in the creative experience. Then a new feeling enters: You are standing outside yourself and watching as the creative impulse seems to run by itself. The Latin roots of the word *ecstasy* refer to this feeling of standing outside.

The more you expand your awareness, the more you will be supported by the flow of creative intelligence. In this way ecstasy becomes a normal mode of life, rather than an unusual or extraordinary experience.

Creative intelligence leaves no footprints in the physical world, but it has been intimately linked with you your entire life. Sometimes you've been focused on testing your abilities, which is what happened during the years of infancy and early childhood. Learning to walk is a great new adventure in applied creativity—balance, coordination, motor control, and vision must come together in an entirely new way. Then you began to use creative intelligence more consciously—learning to read, navigating the great wide world, relating to other people outside your family.

Only by consciously paying attention to the gifts of chit akash can you live with complete assurance that the flow of creative intelligence is supporting you. Unknown to you, complete mastery is within your reach—that's the fascinating possibility we will address next.

# Mapping the Miracle

I f a fertilized egg in the womb is in full command of creative intelligence, why aren't we? The problem lies in one of the attributes of creative intelligence: *a clear path to reach any goal.* Everyone has experienced setbacks and disappointments in the past, and these leave an imprint in memory. Each imprint—being scolded by your parents, doing poorly on a test at school, being ignored by someone you had a crush on—acts like a microchip, sending out the same signal repeatedly.

The repeated discouraging signal says, "You can't. It won't work out. There's trouble ahead. Don't risk it." Imagine a child just old enough to walk by herself to school. She proceeds down the sidewalk, and suddenly from nowhere a dodgeball is thrown at her by someone hidden in the bushes.

The child escapes the ball unhurt, but then every few feet, another dodgeball is hurled at her by unseen hands.

It doesn't matter that some balls hit and others miss. The child is sent into a state of anxiety, awaiting the next threat, which will arrive unpredictably. This is the psychological situation we all find ourselves in. We are vigilant for unpredictable threats, and a hidden microchip beeps out its anxious warning. "You can't. It won't work out. There's trouble ahead. Don't risk it." What makes the situation even more pernicious is that the child walking to school will remain anxious even if the dodgeballs stop being thrown at her. The specter of danger is enough.

This gloomy setup seems to make it impossible to find a clear path through chit akash, the mind space everyone must navigate every day. But the reality is otherwise. You can master every aspect of creative intelligence. The key is to understand how the flow of life actually works. The map is very simple—see below.

Quantum/Causal Body—>
Chit Akash—> Physical Body

Everything creative intelligence brings to you follows this path. An impulse originates in the quantum or causal body. It might be a conscious impulse, like wanting to go outside to enjoy a bright spring day, or a totally unconscious impulse, like the one that keeps your heart muscles beating. The same flow applies to both. It moves through chit akash before it arrives at your physical body.

A great deal is happening when any impulse is making this journey from first cause to final result. In brief, a miracle unfolds. Each impulse knows what it is supposed to do, where it is headed, and how it relates to thousands of other impulses generated by the body every second. Without this knowledge, a seed couldn't grow into a flower. Cut into a seed and you see no stems, roots, leaves, or blossoms in microscopic form. You see only organic chemicals arranged in a certain way through genetics. This mass of chemicals sprouts and unfolds according to well-known biological processes. What is mysterious is how chemicals are transformed to produce a stalk of wheat as opposed to a rosebush. The DNA that makes wheat different from a rosebush is only a blueprint. It doesn't know how to make a plant, just as the blueprint of your house doesn't know how to build a house.

Creative intelligence invisibly supplies the necessary knowledge, and it is supplied in real time, on the fly, without a mistake. Evidence for this is found in the embryonic brain when you were still in the womb. After a few days, a fertilized egg has divided enough times to form a blob of cells known as a zygote. There is no microscopic brain in the blob, yet somehow a brain must be created. This occurs as the zygote becomes an embryo. It is easy to see the nascent beginnings of arms, legs, a torso, and a head starting to form.

Unseen, and quite miraculously, stem cells follow their destined path to differentiate into heart cells, liver cells, brain cells, and so on. In the case of the brain, the process is uncanny, because once a stem cell knows that it is a brain cell, it must journey to the part of the brain it belongs in, such as the visual cortex, the medulla, or the frontal lobes. Milling around in a crowd of brain cells doesn't do the trick. Instead, there are filaments that function as pathways, known as "radial glia." The migrating brain cells use this like a scaffold to find and hold their place in the developing brain.

As remarkable as the process is, there's a mystery involved in how the glial cells, which aren't the same as neurons, know where the right locations are. There are hundreds of specific locations in the brain. For example, a tiny clump of cells enables you to recognize that a certain house is where you live. The only viable answer is creative intelligence that has been creating you, beginning the instant you were conceived.

## The five *koshas*

Mapping the flow of creative intelligence is open to even finer detail—by peeling away every stage of creativity, you will discover that you exist in more than one dimension. According to the Vedic tradition we each have subtle bodies that exist in consciousness. Each body belongs to you and is experienced in different ways.

They are called *koshas*, or "sheaths," in Sanskrit. The koshas give you five bodies, of which the physical body is the least important, because it is the end point, where self-awareness is masked from its quantum source. The five koshas are

**Physical body:** *Annamaya kosha*, an outer-layer sheath, sometimes referred to as the "food sheath."

**Energetic body:** *Pranamaya kosha*, the sheath created by the subtle breath or life energy (prana).

**Mental body:** *Manomaya kosha*, the sheath created by the mind.

**Wisdom body, or body of intellect:** *Vijñānamaya kosha*, the sheath created by inner knowledge.

**Body of bliss:** *Anandamaya kosha*, the sheath composed of bliss-consciousness before any form emerges.

Don't worry about the Sanskrit terminology. What is important about the koshas is that they map the creative process that is occurring in, around, and through you. Your experience shifts according to the level of existence (body) where you put your attention. If you focus on the physical world "out there," you are inhabiting a part of that world—the physical body—which becomes a thing in a universe of things. No self-awareness is needed or even desirable. Your chief activity in the physical world is devoted to avoiding pain and seeking pleasure. From this perspective, your body is a machine, including your brain. If you're asked to explain anything about how the world works, you resort to materialism, which breaks down all phenomena into the physical apparatus that operates them.

The five koshas fill in the map of how consciousness creates everything. The starting point is pure consciousness, which has no qualities, and then the whole process proceeds as shown in the diagram below.

Pure Consciousness —> Bliss-Consciousness —>
Wisdom/Intellect —> Mind —>
Life Energy (Prana) —> Physical World

Knowing that creation unfolds this way is invaluable. It puts the tools of creation in your hands. Most people are creating their life story without this knowledge. They cobble together bits and pieces with a mix of conscious and unconscious actions, thoughts, and emotions. "I hate X" and "I hate Y" drive their desires. Past hurts and achievements dictate behavior in the present. Yet inside this mix of the conscious and the unconscious, everyone has had glimpses of how creation unfolds.

*Pure consciousness* is revealed as the silent gap between thoughts, in deep meditation, and in moments of complete peace.

*Bliss-consciousness* is revealed in moments of joy, rapture, inspiration, and wonder.

*Wisdom* is revealed in moments of insight and intuition.

---

*Mind* is revealed in mental activity.

*Life energy* is self-evident in the feeling of being alive.

The *physical world* is self-evident to the five senses.

The purpose of drawing a line between wisdom and mind is that everything below the line—mind, life energy, and the physical world—is constantly with us. Most people are only dimly aware of the higher levels of wisdom, bliss-consciousness, and pure consciousness.

We are energized to stay alive and to thrive if we can. These functions are organized in the energetic body. If you are so depressed that you feel listless and without purpose, your energetic body has become depleted. In that case, it doesn't matter that your physical body is operating normally (or close to normally, since depression has physical side effects).

You can sense instinctively when your energy is low or depleted, which indicates that the energetic body isn't as inert as the term *sheath* or *shell*, another definition of *kosha*, implies. Self-awareness becomes higher when you begin to think, entering the region of the mental body. Thinking is so basic to existence that the French philosopher René Descartes famously declared, "I think, therefore I am" (*Cogito ergo sum* in Latin). That's debatable. The Vedic rishis would reverse the logic: *I am, therefore, I think*. But leaving philosophy aside, the mind is the next link in the chain of creation.

Personal self-awareness reaches its peak in wisdom, and the wisdom body, also called the "body of intellect," gives you the ability to know. Not just to know individual facts, such as that N'Djamena is the capital of the African country of Chad, or that red blood cells are the only cells in your body that do not contain DNA. Behind anything you know lies the capacity to know in the first place. Wisdom enters the picture because the rishis focused on innate knowledge that doesn't need to be learned, such as how to reason, love, show empathy, have insight, discern truth from lies, and create something new, alongside the capacity for wonder, curiosity, and discovery. Wisdom shouldn't be considered rare, but it becomes rare when people lack self-awareness. It takes great self-awareness to be wise.

The subtlest kosha is the body of bliss. In Vedic terms, the "stuff" of creation isn't material, but conscious. In fact, pure consciousness is the womb of creation. This isn't something you can reason with the intellect or reach in everyday experience. Pure consciousness reveals itself in deep meditation as a kind of dynamism at the heart of creation. The way we channel this dynamism is through the experience of bliss. Bliss is more than joy or ecstasy. Bliss is a primal vibrancy inside a peak experience. It is wrapped in an epiphany when someone suddenly "sees the light."

The five koshas conveniently package your life into levels. How well you navigate these levels determines to a great extent how your life story will play out. Self-awareness can take you as far as the human mind can go, into regions of discovery and curiosity once you reach the body of wisdom. The world has seen incredibly creative people—Picasso was said to have made a piece of art every day—but it is also creative to have insight, to feel self-worth, and to know how to live and be loved.

In its data collection, modern science ignores the subtler koshas that are not physical, excluding everything except physical measurements and investigations confined to the material world. Still, it is impossible to produce good science without insight, discovery, and curiosity. Reality has a way of working outside the rules. Einstein had eloquent things to say about this, including the following: "The most beautiful thing we can experience is the mysterious. It is the source of all true art and science. He to whom this emotion is a stranger, who can no longer pause to wonder and stand rapt in awe, is as good as dead; his eyes are closed."

Our eyes are kept closed as long as we cling to the material world as our only home and survival as the goal of evolution. Survival is a powerful agenda, and we all heed its call. But as soon as you learn about the koshas, it becomes obvious that humans are multidimensional. Each dimension allows you to expand your awareness without boundaries.

A practical start is to devote time every day to the things you most value in life. What ideas intrigue you? What is a desirable creative outlet? How can you be inspired? Your aim is creative living, the very opposite of a life ruled by routine, habit, and received opinion. Give yourself the experience you need to escape the confinement of the physical body. Here are a few points to consider.

- Visualize the color blue in your mind. Now walk around the room, keeping the color in mind. Ask yourself if blue went anywhere just because your body did.

- While washing the dishes or taking a bath, bring a happy memory to mind. Ask yourself if your memory gets wet when your body does.

- Sing a favorite song to yourself, a tune that millions of people know. Ask yourself if the tune is yours or a shared experience in collective consciousness. As part of collective consciousness, you don't feel less like yourself. In fact, if you've ever gone to a concert and gotten caught up in the audience's enjoyment, don't you feel more intensely alive, more like yourself?

- Read a poem, some spiritual writing, or a piece of wisdom that inspires you. An individual "I" spoke those words, but what was needed to create inspiration? No individual, not even a single culture. Inspiration is innate. You feel it when you feel it, a moment of spontaneous recognition that wasn't invented by you or anyone else.

These are small examples of how to claim your true, multidimensional nature.

# PART THREE

# Expand Your Awareness: Seven Quantum Breakthroughs

# The Promise of a Breakthrough

This section of the book aims to help you experience a breakthrough, or an "aha!" moment. A breakthrough creates change as nothing else can. You suddenly see something you never saw.

The opposite of a breakthrough is inertia, routine, habit, and business as usual. Routine is comfortable—we all live 90 percent of everyday life following set patterns and unconscious habits with few deviations. But living this way has a fatal flaw: If you keep doing the same old thing, you will get the same result. Routines and habits make breakthroughs impossible.

Everyday life keeps you from knowing with total certainty who you are and why you are here. Instead, everyone at some time or other experiences bouts of insecurity, doubt, confusion, and inner conflict. To overcome this, you can do one of two things.

You can build up a set of habits, routines, and set beliefs that serve to reinforce the story you have chosen to live. Without knowing why your story exists, you cling to it. The hidden motivation behind all stories is to make the ego-personality feel real, so that it can move forward without constantly feeling insecure.

The other choice is to seek breakthroughs that lead to expanded awareness—not just a single "aha" moment, but many. Each one brings you closer to your quantum source, allowing you to say, with more and more confidence, "I know who I am." In other words, you experience a shift in identity, which cannot happen all at once. It's an evolutionary process. Or as the Vedic seers declared, "This isn't knowledge you learn. This is knowledge you become."

Just beneath the surface, two forces are contending for your attention, although you are probably unaware of them. One is the force of inertia; the other is the force of evolution. Inertia tries to keep everything the same; evolution tries to explore the new and unknown. You can let these forces play out without intervening. The outcome, however, will be beyond your control. Evolution is a creative choice.

You can step into the new anytime you want to. But the process needs to unfold naturally. No two people evolve along the same path.

*It is possible to evolve without fear of the unknown. Risk taking isn't necessary or helpful. Instead, as you connect with quantum reality, it guides you from within. The beauty of a breakthrough is that it emerges at the right time, as if the tumblers of a lock have suddenly aligned. For that to happen, something somewhere must know who you are and foresee what is best for you. Your thinking mind doesn't possess this knowledge—it is preoccupied with your story and keeping it going. Nor can your unconscious mind hold this knowledge, since it contains suppressed fears, old hurts, and years of conditioning.*

The only candidate for knowing who you really are lies at the level where all experiences are created. By now you realize that this level of existence is the causal body or the quantum body—one is the ancient Vedic term, the other is the modern scientific term. But they are equivalents. Once you connect with your quantum body, you are connected to the "real" reality. For here, all things are possible.

Now you need to make this promise a living reality.

## How this section works

This section will work only if you are willing to evolve. It is therefore crucial to keep in mind what evolution is not.

It is not the same as the story you are living right now.

It is not something you achieve by thinking.

It is not painful or frightening.

It is not a process of self-improvement.

The last point might give us pause; most people don't seek to evolve. They prefer to improve their story, which is certainly desirable. Your story has two sides—positive and negative. Who wouldn't want to increase the positive? But from the quantum perspective, the best story in the world, one that contains nothing negative in any way, is simply an upgrade of the illusion. Self-improvement takes place at the level of the ego-personality. It might change your life for the better on the surface, but it won't help you to understand who you really are.

The prospect of evolution makes the ego-personality nervous. It is anxious that its sense of carefully built secu-

rity is threatened. But your ego can only build false secu-
rity. A Vedic saying declares, "Remove all illusions, and
what remains must be real." Far from being a threat, evolution crosses the threshold into bliss, love, compassion,
truth, beauty, and creativity. Once you begin the journey,
you can live your entire life across that threshold.

Quantum reality is timeless, and therefore evolution
never ends. It creates an ascending arc until you reach the
place where you can say, as the Vedic rishis did, "That
which looks through your eyes is God. Look at anything,
and you will realize God."

# #1

## Reality Is Experience.

The most revolutionary ideas can look very simple. Reality is experience. At first, this idea seems obvious. Light is real because you can see, which is an experience. Sound is real because you can hear, another experience. But there's a depth charge hidden in those two statements. Light isn't real if you can't see, and sound isn't real if you can't hear.

Expand this to cover all five senses. What you get is explosive: *Nothing can be real without an experience.*

If that statement is true, then the world gets turned upside down. We are conditioned to believe that reality is independent of experience. The building blocks of the cosmos, science declares, are physical. Starting with subatomic particles and reaching to the farthest galaxy billions of light-years away, you will find nothing but "things" large and small. These things are assumed to be real without question. Pile the simplest things up and you start to get bigger things. Quarks eventually lead to galaxies; RNA to human DNA.

It seems absurd that this viewpoint could be misleading. The flaw is revealed only by going to the *cause* of everything, not the *stuff* of everything. The stuff of a violin is wood, glue, and wire, but the cause of a violin—its only reason to exist—is music. Without the experience of music, a violin might as well be a doorstop. In the same way, all of reality is solely justified by what we experience.

We experience music even without the slightest knowledge of how to make a violin. We experience being alive without a degree in chemistry. A skeptic might argue that gravity or the speed of light doesn't need to be experienced; gravity and the speed of light have been around since the Big Bang 13.8 billion years ago. But if you turn that proposition upside down, you realize that nothing about gravity or the speed of light means anything until it affects a human being. Gravity affects you when you fall or drop a penny from the top of the Empire State Building, which you can't do. (So many coins are dropped from the Empire State Building that the observation deck had to be constructed so that a thrown coin lands on a flat surface before it can reach the street below. Fortunately, even without this safety net, a coin thrown from the top of the Empire State Building can't hurt you.)

The way that gravity is associated with falling makes it seem like a force pulling objects to the ground. But gravity isn't a force. As Einstein made clear with the General Theory of Relativity, gravity is actually a curvature in spacetime. It is only called the "force of gravity" for the sake of convenience, just as we say *sunrise* and *sunset* even though the sun doesn't move across the sky at all.

When you explore Nature deeply enough, the physical things that seem so reliable vanish. At the quantum level, subatomic particles wink in and out of existence. As they do, they take space and time with them, for the tiniest fraction of a millisecond. Here also gravity comes into being. What causes it to come into being? That's the right question to ask, because now we are at the level of the causal body, and only the root cause will reveal the truth about anything.

Is the causal body also an experience? No. The causal body is where existence is getting ready to create experiences. Your mind, which traffics in experience, can't grasp its own creation, the same way a baby cannot remember anything that happened to it before it was born. As long as you are in the realm of creation, however, the mind is inseparable from how creation works. In other words, cosmic creation has a human component.

This is a breakthrough idea because it defies the accepted notion that the universe is separate and independent of us. To make this more personal, ask yourself why you have a body. Is it an independent mass of cells, tissues, and organs existing on its own? Or is it an extension of you? The second answer makes more sense. A clue is offered by a strange medical phenomenon involving heart-transplant patients. A certain number of these patients experience hallucinations and even temporary psychosis after surgery.

A much smaller number report suddenly having memories that aren't their own, with evidence pointing to the possibility that these memories actually belonged to the person who died and donated his heart. If the human heart was just a lump of pulsating muscle, these phenomena shouldn't exist. It is almost as if the patient experiencing a stranger's memories had received a brain transplant. The answer is that all cells, not just brain cells, participate in the creative process that goes into someone's bodymind from birth onward. The whole point of having a body, in fact, is to experience the world and your place in it. Lose that, and you have lost the experience of life.

We all know this instinctively. We look at existence through the lens of personal experience. For example, you can examine a car accident and explain it in terms of the damaged parts scattered and crumpled at the accident scene. Yet something human—a drunk driver, for example, or someone being on a cell phone instead of watching the road—tells you what caused the accident. Eliminating the human element turns a car accident into a meaningless physical event.

Physical explanations tell us how things happen; experience tells us why. This sounds like semantics, but the gap between "how" and "why" makes all the difference when it comes to love, compassion, insight, creativity, devotion, intelligence, and spiritual awakening. The "how" is a physical event, which can be located in the brain and tracked back to molecules, atoms, and subatomic particles. Somewhere along the way, as with a car accident, the experience is lost. Without a doubt love isn't real until you experience it, and the same holds true for the rest of the list.

Now you can see why "Reality is experience" looks simple but contains a depth charge. Inside those words is everything cherished in human existence.

# 2

# The World Is Magic.
## You Are the Magician.

Figuring out reality is a hard slog. It has taken more than two millennia—ever since the ancient Greek concept of the atom was introduced—to peer into the finest workings of creation. What makes the journey ironic is that the atom was a flawed concept. An atom by definition was supposed to be the tiniest thing in creation, but at the quantum level things vanish, and what takes their place is vibrations. It is hard to look at planet Earth as a twang on a cosmic guitar string, and, of course, the details get much more complicated. But vibrations are so crucial to modern physics that even beyond the quantum field, the pre-created state is thought to be the domain of vibrating superstrings (even though there is no possibility of seeing them, since superstrings come into being before time and space emerge).

Once you figure out how every vibration interacts with every other one (an impossible task), the entire cosmos would reveal its hidden structure. If this sounds like the end of the story, it isn't even the beginning. Vibrations are the ultimate example of "You can't get there from here." Something magical happens to vibrations that defies a physical explanation. Experience is born. The beauty we experience viewing a Rembrandt self-portrait, seeing a newborn baby, or listening to Bach—all this is the product of a magic act, and you are the magician.

## Begin with vibrations

To embrace your role as a magician, you first must go deeper into vibrations. Whatever your psychology might be at this moment, from hopeless and depressed to joyful and optimistic, it began as a vibration in the quantum field. The more cosmic the vibration, the less connected it is to you as an individual reading this book. So where was your good or bad mood born? This question sounds abstract, but it takes us across the threshold to where the magic is born.

Whatever you see, hear, touch, taste, or smell is vibrational, and so is the quantum field itself. But you don't experience your five senses as vibrations. What you experience are qualia, the qualities of life that make experience possible (the word *qualia* was introduced on page 93). By themselves, the vibrations in the quantum field display no qualia. Not only is the quantum field not happy or sad, it contains no light, sound, scents, or any other qualia. They arise only through consciousness; they are the essence, in fact, of creative intelligence.

As the pioneering British neurologist Sir John Eccles declared, "I want you to realize that there is no color in the natural world and no sounds—nothing of this kind—no textures, no patterns, no beauty, no scent . . ." This seems unbelievable at first glance. You are like a magician fooled by his own tricks.

Eccles goes on to explain why we need to embrace the magic as our own. "The 'world out there' is synthesized in our consciousness." Everyone knows the riddle "If a tree falls in the forest with no one around, does it make a sound?" The answer is no. Sound needs someone to hear it; otherwise, it doesn't exist. Photons must land on the retina of your eye and send neural impulses traveling through your visual cortex to make visible light, but photons by themselves are invisible.

The Vedic rishis made this breakthrough first, as often happens. To them, the causal body isn't located "out there" in time and space, because the causal body creates time and space. You emerge at every second from the shadow zone between creation and pre-creation—and you bring with you every qualia that gives your life meaning. It isn't surprising that we fall for such an astonishing, all-enveloping magical theater, which is known as *maya* in the Vedic tradition. The Sanskrit word is usually translated into English as "illusion," but a better translation is "distraction." At the beginning, every student of magic is told that stage illusion depends on distracting the audience. Most of us, in fact, would rather sit in the audience and be amazed by the lady sawed in half than be onstage knowing that the whole thing is a trick. But with maya the case is the reverse. Only by knowing how the trickery works can you know the secret of creation.

It is the last two steps—perception and interpretation—that create the magic of sound, sight, touch, taste, and smell. A certain range of the visible spectrum is magically transformed into the red of a rose, for instance, to which the perceiver adds the rose's plush texture and its heady perfume. The reason that *magic* is a legitimate term for this transformation is that you can't mix and match vibrations to arrive at qualia. An example will make the situation clearer.

A baby crying in the next room is never just a collection of vibrations, carrying energy and information. It's an event waiting to be interpreted. Is the baby's cry something to be alarmed over, a sign of illness or distress? Is it just a passing moment of crankiness or a signal that the baby is hungry and needs milk? Those interpretations are crucial. The data being generated are irrelevant.

The Vedic rishis, on the other hand, declared that *vibrations already contain experience*. This notion has revolutionary implications. The meaning of any experience is packaged with the vibrations that spark a chain of events. The entire journey that begins with a faint vibration in the quantum field has you in mind every step of the way, because the aim is to give you (and every other living creature) a meaningful experience. The apparatus of wave amplitudes, energy states, position in time and space, etc., is necessary, but it bears no resemblance to a meaningful experience any more than the clacking of saxophone keys tells us anything about a great jazz performance or the opening and closing of a baby's vocal cords tells us anything about what the baby is feeling. Likewise, you can't quantify love, beauty, truth, creativity, and inner growth.

The body you see in the bathroom mirror is part of the maya that keeps you on the surface of life. As magic goes, this trick is incredibly convincing. No one walks around viewing the body as if, like a movie, it were just artificial imagery. If we weren't creating the magic, maya would be a cruel deception. Once you accept your role creating the magic, however, maya becomes what it has always been, pure theater. Its trickery is only so much stage business.

You might feel a nostalgic twinge for the time when you sat in the audience, but only in passing. It is far better to wake up and discover the infinite possibilities that come from being conscious. Far more is gained than will ever be lost, since what you wind up losing was distracting you from reality.

# #3

## The Experiencer Is Eternal.

Uncovering one mystery tends to reveal another one, which is exactly what happens once you accept your role as a magician. Since you are making a private decision that occurs only "in here," how does that change the world? You can decide that you are a rock star or an entrepreneur, but that doesn't necessarily make you one. What's so special about this particular decision? It's not as if you handed yourself the key to the magic, and no one else did, either.

To clarify matters, imagine yourself strolling in the park, soaking up the summer sunshine. Who is having this experience? You, of course—the answer is so simple that we take it for granted. But there are some hidden implications that reveal more about reality. All day your experiences come and go. The events of half an hour ago are gone forever unless something memorable happened. Yet you the experiencer didn't come and go. Built into every experiencer is the ability to hold reality together. Otherwise, we'd be a slave to sense impressions, the way a baby turns its head at any loud sound and gazes at any bright color. The baby hasn't found the experiencer inside, and, in the disaster of advanced Alzheimer's disease, the experiencer is lost.

The experiencer can get lost even in normal adult life. When you tune out, get distracted, stop paying attention, grow drowsy, or feel overwhelmed with anxiety, all these are examples of the experiencer losing contact with their own reality. Your state of awareness has changed. Thanks to how vulnerable we are to life's ups and downs, we are blinded to the fact that an eternal, unchanging experiencer *must* exist. There is a rare brain disorder that causes the loss of sight, sound, hearing, touch, taste, and smell altogether. Still, the experiencer knows that this total loss has occurred. Deep dreamless sleep might seem to blot out all experiences, yet advanced yogis testify that they remain completely self-aware in the deepest sleep—in fact, they declare that this is an experience of ultimate peace and bliss.

## The witness

The Vedic rishis called the eternal experiencer the witness. For the witness to be real, you must experience it. That's easy enough when an experience catches your attention. Gazing at a Hubble telescope photo that reveals spinning galaxies as numerous as grains of sand on the beach, you can feel such awe that you stop thinking and simply exist as a silent witness. What is harder is to experience the unchangeable nature of this witness. If you can do that, you will realize that all your life you have never come from anywhere or gone anywhere. The only reason this sounds mystical or incredible is your wandering attention.

Wandering attention is all it takes to forget who you really are. Cats are mesmerized by laser pointers. Shine a red laser dot on the floor, and once your cat spots it, the chase is on. The cat will follow the laser everywhere it moves. It would be a mistake to sneer, "Dumb cat," because people chase after fixations just as obsessively. The next pleasure you might have doesn't exist yet; it is just a possibility. Yet who doesn't run after the phantom of pleasure? If you are in the habit of worrying, it does little good to be told that 99 percent of what you worry about will never happen. A worrying mind never loses its habit of anxious fixation.

When you ask the question that began this chapter, "Who is having the experience?," the answer doesn't have to be a human being. A cell, tissue, organ, system, and the whole body represent levels of experience that are entirely different. Yet one silent, unchanging experiencer unites them all. The trail leads to one conclusion: At every level of Nature, consciousness looks through the lens of the witness. The witness is being favored whenever you

Feel deep contentment

Experience the satisfaction of being here now

Think few nagging thoughts

Don't fall prey to anxiety

Cease worrying about what might happen next

Stop fixating on the things you lack

Appreciate the gifts you are given now

Enjoy inner calm and quiet peace

Experience a full heart

Feel that you belong

Such moments occur in everyone's life, but we don't notice or value them enough. When you go to sleep at night or should you fall into a coma, the witness never shifts its attention away, and your body is taken care of. Somehow consciousness knows what to do even when our attention wanders away. The eternal witness is necessary in every level of existence, which is why it is much better to be in touch with the witness than to lose contact with it. The witness isn't passive. The witness is dynamic, with possibilities on the very edge of creation.

You can easily catch a glimpse of the witness by observing your mind right this minute. Notice your next thought or feeling as it arises. The experience is fleeting. As the thought or feeling fades away, there is a gap of silence. This silence is far from empty, however. From it will spring your next thought or feeling. In fact, the witness is how you are able to have thoughts and feelings. The witness adds the component of silent awareness.

Therefore, the witness isn't a choice. You can't do without it, just as a movie can't do without the screen. If the witness were simply passive, there would be little obvious value to identifying with it. It is far more exciting to identify with the ego and its drama. But dramas are famous for being unpredictable, and any story line can take a bad turn. If you live from the level of your story, which is mind-made, you are basing everything on shifting sands. The ego realizes this at some level, which is why it resorts to clinging like a starfish holding tightly to a rock to keep the tide from sweeping it away. What works for starfish doesn't work for humans, however.

Once you understand about the witness, you will notice it more often, and then you can aim to be in constant contact with it. You already know that you are the experiencer when it comes to the five senses. For many people, this is basically enough. Preoccupied with sensual desires—not just sexual desire but all the desirable things to be seen, heard, touched, tasted, and smelled—they have a full plate in front of them. They have no curiosity about who the experiencer really is, or why anybody should care.

This situation can be turned around with a simple exercise. Sit quietly and do the exercise after you read the description. After putting the book down, notice your thoughts coming and going. It doesn't matter if the thoughts are trivial or important. Any train of thought works the same way. The thought arises and fades away.

There is a gap of silence, then the next thought arises and fades away. Having made this simple observation, return to the book.

The reason you can think isn't revealed in your thoughts, surprising as that sounds. Look at the following stream of letters: heparedapairofpears. The sequence only acquires meaning by spacing the letters (He pared a pair of pears). Likewise, it takes a gap of silence between your thoughts to enable you to think. This gap isn't blank. It contains intelligence. That's why you can distinguish pare, pair, and pear. Their sound gives nothing away. You have to dip into your silent knowledge to understand the difference, and when you dip into this knowledge, you *don't actually do anything*. The knowledge is simply part of your consciousness.

In the gap between thoughts, all knowledge is contained. You don't have an immense storehouse of note cards that you consult. In this exercise you fell back on the witness, where knowledge exists. The experiencer, it turns out, is also the knower. Without doing anything at all, you are witnessing all kinds of knowledge that makes your existence possible. For example,

- You know that you exist and are alive.
- You know where you are.
- You know that you are you and not someone else.

- You know what your thoughts mean.
- You know how to focus your attention.
- You know how to stop paying attention.
- You know how to select the words for what you want to say.
- You know where there are gaps in your knowledge.
- You know how to operate your muscles.

Once you begin, this list of silent knowledge can be expanded almost endlessly. Silent knowledge requires no energy; therefore, the brain, which does require energy for every process, however minuscule, isn't the home of the experiencer or the witness. The experiencer is its own home. You visit it at home in the gaps between every thought.

Now an enticing possibility opens up. If silent knowledge creates all thoughts, maybe it creates all experiences, since thought isn't our only experience "in here." We have the experience of dreaming, imagining, wondering, feeling, sensing, seeing inner images, etc. Without the witness, none of that would be possible. There must be a gap between any two experiences, and the witness is at home in the gap. Suddenly silent inner knowledge looms large as the most necessary thing in the world.

# #4

## Infinity Is the New Normal.

To find out who you really are, we must go to a place hardly anyone ever thinks about—infinity. We're more comfortable inside a smaller frame of reference. The physical body is a natural frame of reference, since it needs care and feeding every day and serves as a shelter from the outside world, like a woodcutter's hut in the forest. Even though the human body is impermanent and subject to disease and aging, we identify this frail life-support system as "my" body. By comparison, infinity is far, far out of reach. The infinite, from a physical point of view, is unimaginable.

But if you consider the quantum body "my" body, you would immediately become an infinite being, because the quantum body takes on the reality of the quantum field, which is infinite in all directions. This might not sound like an advantage, but consider this. The quantum field never ages or gets sick. As astonishing as the human genome is, the DNA in your cells degrades with time. One of the most damaging degradations occurs at the very tip of a strand of DNA, which is called a telomere. Telomeres create a tightly defined end cap to each strand of DNA, like the period at the end of this sentence. But over time telomeres become fuzzy and frayed, like the fuzzy end of a piece of old yarn. When this happens, your DNA can no longer replicate as efficiently as it should, and your body becomes more susceptible to aging.

Your quantum body never frays, never degrades over time, because the infinite has no beginning or end. There's a famous passage in the Bhagavad-Gita where Lord Krishna speaks to the warrior Arjuna about the hidden essence of life. "Weapons cannot cut It, nor can fire burn It; water cannot wet It, nor can wind dry It." For centuries, *It* has referred to the divine nature in all of us; the spiritual seeker's aim is to find It and live according to It. You might take Krishna's words as an article of faith, no different from having faith in any religious text.

Yet in the modern secular world *It* is better described as the quantum body. The very fact that it is abstract saves us from the illusion that God or the gods are fickle humans on a gigantic scale, subject to mood swings, vengeance, and erratic mercy. The quantum body exists in an infinite field that has no personal quirks; therefore, it is never angry or loving toward you on a whim. (Being objective, no one has ever proved that God feels those emotions, either.) Instead, the quantum body is the origin of every experience anyone has ever had or will have. We should look upon infinity as normal. As a frame of reference, it encompasses everything human, extending our reach beyond the finite.

## The eternal journey

Infinity is hard to grasp. It doesn't refer to something very big, or big beyond imagining. It refers to something that doesn't fit in time and space—in other words, the unbounded. How could this possibly apply to everyday life? Take the largest library in the world (which isn't the Library of Congress but the Berlin State Library, at 23.4 million books), and you can double its size by translating each book into a second language. Add translations in all the world's living languages, which are estimated to be around 7,000, and the library is in the billions. Change the first word in each book, then the second word, the third, and so on, and the number of books rises to the trillions.

This sounds temptingly like a good way to reach infinity, but in fact it isn't—no matter how large the library became, the number of books would still be finite. Yet we access infinity all the time in a much simpler way. Every word you speak, every thought you think, uses a limited number of words drawn from a limited vocabulary. This is transformed into infinity by relying on creativity. Without knowing all the words in the *Oxford English Dictionary*, which number 600,000 over the last thousand years, you can think or say something original just with the words you know. No matter how many sentences have been spoken by all the people who have ever lived, an equal number remain to be spoken—in fact, an infinite number, because there is no conceivable end to what a human being can say. (Mathematically, this is proven by the fact that no matter how long a string of numbers might be, you can always add one to it, ad infinitum.)

Human beings inhabit a field of infinite possibilities, not just in words and thoughts, but in actions, dreams, aspirations, relationships, etc. So, what are you doing with your share of infinity? Your answer might be severely truncated if you are depressed, poor, and lonely, or it might be prodigious, if you are the next Einstein. Yet the existence of infinite possibilities never changes. Everyone shares in the same eternal journey from here to infinity. No doubt you've seen the mathematical symbol for infinity (see below).

The symbol is ancient and found in many cultures, in particular, the Vikings', where it was central to their mythology. But what this symbol represents is far more ancient: eternity, or life without end. Tracing the infinity symbol, you never find its beginning or end; this is like the snake biting its tail, mythically named the Ouroboros. But if you rotate the symbol 90 degrees, you get something surprising: the eternal journey that everyone and everything is on.

This doesn't look like the map of a journey until we make a tweak to it.

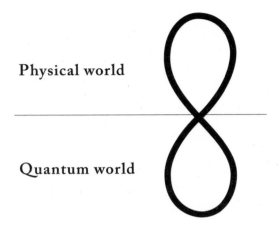

**Physical world**

**Quantum world**

Reality is fluid. Everything travels in a loop between the physical (or macroscopic) world and the quantum domain. What you experience daily is happening at the crossroads of infinity. That the path is a feedback loop is all-important. Unlike an ice skater tracing the same figure 8 with perfect precision, you are transformed every time you travel above and below the line that separates your physical and quantum bodies.

It takes only the tiniest impulse to shake the whole feedback system, something like the Butterfly Effect, by which the flapping of a single butterfly's wing can cause enough alteration in the weather to trigger a hurricane somewhere else. The example is drawn from chaos theory and is meant as a metaphor for tiny causes leading to big effects. In human terms, replace the butterfly's flapping wings with the words *I love you* whispered in your ear, as opposed to the words *Your bank account is empty.* Instantly your whole body reacts, marked by alterations in blood pressure, heart rate, the hormones racing through your bloodstream. A tiny cause can shake your whole reality if the consequences are serious enough.

The logical conclusion is that the journey to and from the quantum domain leads to an infinite number of transformations that can occur in mind and body. The next thought or word could be trivial, earthshaking, or anything in between. As a frame of reference, nothing is more human than infinity.

# 5

## The Brain Is Not the Mind.

Theories can be judged by what they leave out as much as by what they include, and the less they leave out, the better. A whopping amount is left out when any theory mistakes the brain for the mind. This is such a common assumption that for the vast majority of neuroscientists Brain = Mind. If you make this mistake, you will decide that sight is created by the visual cortex, hearing by the auditory cortex, smell by the olfactory bulb, and so on.

With a detailed brain map, so the thinking goes, neuroscience will be able to point to the exact clump of brain cells where every thought and sensation is created. The fatal flaw with this view is that the brain doesn't have any experiences—it merely transmits what the mind is experiencing. If you know algebra, does your brain know algebra? If you love chocolate, does your brain love chocolate? Does your brain get depressed, elated, anxious, or triumphant? The correct answer to all these questions is no. So why does medical science continue to assert that the brain is responsible for the mind?

One reason is the streetlight effect, which got its name from an old joke. A man is crawling on his hands and knees under a streetlight. A passerby asks what he is doing, and the man says, "I'm looking for my keys." The passerby gets down on his hands and knees to help, but after a few minutes he says, "Are you sure you lost your keys here?"

"No," the main replies, "I lost them in the park."

"Then why are you looking here?" the passerby asks.

"Because this is where the light is," says the man.

The streetlight effect, therefore, is about a bias for looking where the light is easiest. It is much easier to look at the brain than the mind, and on CT scans and fMRIs, the images literally light up. Not only that, but they light up in areas associated with different kinds of mental activity. In past decades, brain scans were crude, in that they measured small changes in blood flow that appear "hot" or "cold" on the image. But the technology is now so advanced that some innovative researchers claim to spot exactly what a person is thinking or feeling, according to brain activity in very precise patterns.

But if you believe that this evidence is enough to say

Brain = Mind, you have deprived consciousness of its own existence. Consciousness is just another pattern of hot and cold spots in the brain—in other words, a by-product—like the heat given off by a bonfire. You are saying that matter comes before mind, which is the opposite of what this book says.

## The great divide

The argument over "mind first" or "matter first" has created a great divide, which seemingly concerns only scientists and philosophers, but, in reality, everyone's life is affected. If you don't accept that consciousness is the origin of creation, you throw out creative intelligence at the same time, along with related concepts, like the wisdom of the body. Even the mind-body connection becomes suspect if everything has a physical cause.

It's worthwhile to pause for a moment to list the other flaws of assuming that the brain creates consciousness; in other words, the mind.

## Why the Brain Isn't the Mind

The brain contains ordinary atoms and molecules. Atoms and molecules don't think.

The brain has no light or sound inside its gray, mushy tissues. There are no pictures or music in your brain, yet somehow you see pictures and hear music.

No one knows how the brain can assemble a complete three-dimensional world out of billions of bits of scattered data. This would be like adding more wires to a telephone system and claiming that it had learned to speak English.

The brain has no location for the self, the "I" we all identify with.

Vital operations like storing and retrieving memory are totally unexplained. The areas of the brain where memory is stored are like bookshelves; only, in place of books, what these areas store is invisible, and why one memory is stored and not another remains inexplicable.

There is no proof that the brain has experiences of any kind. It has only electrochemical activity.

This list of inconsistencies, gaps, and unproven conjectures should be enough to convince anyone that the brain doesn't create the mind. Even in common speech we say, "I changed my mind" and "I haven't made up my mind yet," not "I changed my brain" or "I haven't made up my brain yet." These expressions are about decision-making. A piano doesn't choose which piece of music to play. People pause before making a decision as simple as choosing from a restaurant menu or as complicated as getting married or changing jobs. The brain has no pause button. Every signal happens instantaneously in the present moment, so it is hard to credit that gray matter lingers over a restaurant menu before it decides what to order.

But the real problem is hidden from sight. Your brain will never lead you to expanded awareness or higher states of consciousness. It is a fixed piece of equipment. There is flexibility built into how the equipment operates, known as "neuroplasticity," by which damaged areas can grow new brain cells. All your life new connections are being made from one brain cell to the next, using filaments called "dendrites" (so named because they branch out like a tree, and *dendro* is Greek for "tree").

Despite this remarkable range of flexibility, the brain cannot evolve in the here and now; the higher brain that *Homo sapiens* possesses above all other creatures took millions of years to evolve. Thought, however, can evolve instantaneously; moreover, it must evolve. Otherwise, we'd still be thinking like infants and would never have learned how to read. Gaining any new skill is evolutionary, and it is always driven by the mind. In a practical sense, "mind first" is part of our instruction manual at birth.

If you want to have the highest experiences in life— love, compassion, peace, creativity, insight, intelligence, empathy, and inner growth—they must be found in consciousness. The motivation to search lies in consciousness because, by its nature, creative intelligence makes only evolutionary choices. It is self-evolving, whereas the brain, even though it is receptive to change, functions largely on old conditioning and relies on its default settings.

We should celebrate therefore that the brain isn't the mind. Neuroscience promises great advances in the future, and medicine has benefited enormously from brain imaging. But it's worth remembering that no matter how miraculous the next medical advance might be, only the mind created Shakespeare. About that, the brain has nothing to say.

# #6

## "I" Is a Bad Habit.

From a quantum perspective, the ego is a bad habit that we haven't learned to break. The most common words in the English language are "be," "and," and "of," but in everyday use, "I" rises to the top. It focuses what we think, say, and do, separating the individual from every other "I" in the world. Thanks to the ego, you don't blend into a crowd of people like identical waves in the ocean. Yet from the viewpoint of the quantum field (and the Vedic tradition would agree as well), you are like a wave on the ocean.

This isn't metaphysical hairsplitting. Your very identity depends on it. Are you separate, isolated, and on your own, or are you part of the whole, merging with cosmic existence? This doesn't seem like a practical choice as far as most people are concerned (if they've ever heard of such a choice in the first place, which is doubtful). For the vast majority, "I" long ago established their life agenda, which is set up as a crooked path zigzagging between "I want X" and "I don't want Y."

Each of us has lived with "I" walking close beside us, monitoring everything that happens, creating the story that has "I" as its center-stage protagonist. So naturally does "I" fit into the scheme of your life that you could hardly credit that "I" is a mental invention, and a fatally flawed one at that. Go back to an axiom that has cropped up before now: *Nothing is real unless it is real for you.* If you view the world through the lens of an isolated, confined, separate identity—the definition of "I"—only the physical world is real.

The habit of "I" masks your true self. You are not an isolated mind enclosed in a physical body. You are the flow of creative intelligence. At your source, where the causal and quantum body merge, you are consciousness itself. This is your true status, whereas everything your ego tells you is bound up in self-doubt, insecurity, and fear. "What about me?" and "What's going to happen to me?" are the most common of anxious thoughts.

## The five *kleshas*

In psychiatric practice, the field known as "ego psychology" is far too complex for a layperson to understand. But the Vedic rishis cut to the chase by reducing the faults of "I" to five mistakes that are the root cause of pain and suffering. They called these the *kleshas*. No matter what you fear will happen to you, no matter how wild your imagination of worst-case scenarios, one of the five kleshas is at work. But the whole point is that the kleshas are false. They raise the specter of suffering in the mind even when no suffering is occurring.

In everyday language, the five kleshas are

1. Ignorance (the inability to tell the real from the false)
2. Egoism (identifying with "I," the individual self)
3. Attachment (clinging to certain things, the objects of desire)
4. Aversion (rejecting other things, the objects of revulsion)
5. Fear of death

These five sources of suffering are all mind-made. They don't exist in the quantum body or in your physical body, either—a liver or heart cell has no problems with ego or attachment. Cells are devoid of the fear of death; in fact, programmed death (biologically known as "apoptosis") is part of a cell's design to make way for new life.

Part of the ego's agenda is to keep you from confronting your deepest fears, but they exist just beneath the surface and entangle you with the five kleshas. As the Vedic rishis saw it, getting entangled is totally unnecessary. What the mind has made, the mind can unmake. Let's do this one klesha at a time.

## 1. Ignorance (the inability to tell the real from the false)

If the first klesha is cleared up, it takes care of the other four; therefore, it is the most important. Ignorance is the product of mistaking yourself for an isolated being trapped in a physical body. "I am this body" is completely false. "I am in this body" is just as false. The reality is that the physical body is the product of the flow of creative intelligence. It is a process happening when consciousness morphs into the physical world. "I am consciousness itself" bursts the illusion created by ignorance.

## 2. Egoism (identifying with "me," the individual self)

Once the first klesha takes hold, creating isolation inside a physical body, the ego grows in importance. "I" is assigned the duty to survive inside the body, and a stream of desires pours out in response to pleasure and pain. The ego becomes a person's identity. Instead of recognizing that "I am consciousness," everyone believes in "I am my story, and I want the best story for myself that I can get."

## 3. Attachment (clinging to certain things, the objects of desire)

Once you identify with your story, some experiences are more desirable than others. The next step is to become attached to those desires. "I" merges into "mine." All the things you surround yourself with to feel more worthy and successful—a solid career, a nice house, money in the bank, etc.—become very hard to let go of. Possessing them is so personal that attachment comes to dominate your existence.

## 4. Aversion (rejecting other things, the objects of revulsion)

The opposite of attachment is aversion—we reject the things we don't want as strongly as we cling to the things we do want. Aversion to physical pain is natural, but far more powerful is psychological aversion. If you broke your ankle on the playground as a child, that pain probably made no lasting impression. But if you were humiliated in school, an aversion to being humiliated again has a lasting grip, usually for a lifetime.

## 5. Fear of death

The ultimate aversion is death, which is feared as a kind of annihilation. This klesha rounds out the repercussions of the first klesha, because if you identify with your body, you will identify with its death. Any time you protect your body from harm, grow anxious about aging, or feel threatened by illness, the shadow of the fear of death passes over you. The illusion is that "My body is gone" equates with "I will be gone at the same time."

All five kleshas are negated by a single realization, "I am consciousness itself." There is no need to confront one klesha at a time. Place your focus on the flow of creative intelligence, and it has the ability to clear the path for you. Your sense of self can escape the confinement of the physical body, which "I" has turned into a shield against reality.

# #7

## Existence Is Your Crowning Glory.

Existence is your crowning glory? Of all the quantum breakthroughs, this final one is the most mystifying. At first glance, there is nothing glorious about existence, which brings both pain and pleasure, ecstasy and suffering. If you wanted to name the crowning glory of being human, many other answers look more appealing: our creativity, our ability to love, our self-awareness. Even the unbelievable complexity of human DNA and the human brain would rank at the summit for many scientists.

But none of those things embraces the complete mystery and miracle of being human. You might say that the past 200,000 years since *Homo sapiens* first appeared have been spent exploring that mystery and that miracle: Human beings are fascinated by who we really are, and no single aspect of our existence, not even love, creativity, and self-awareness, are enough. Something is always left out. There is always a new horizon to cross.

There is nowhere you can go to find the ultimate answers except for existence itself. Existence contains everything, which is why in ancient India the all-encompassing unity of existence was named *Brahman*, from the Sanskrit root that means "to grow or expand." Brahman is the ultimate reality because it can expand infinitely. No matter how much of creation it embraces, there is infinite room left for more.

Because it is all-embracing, Brahman cannot have any shape, size, or location. To be complete, *all-embracing* must include not just the past, present, and future but also *every possible* past, present, and future. The concept is mind-boggling. Every thought you've ever had spins off as part of a new timeline, and what you call your life is just the timeline you chose, and keep choosing, from moment to moment. The other timelines aren't part of your experience, yet they exist, the phantoms of roads not taken.

Such a scheme is inconceivable. Yet Brahman isn't an abstract notion. You are personally included. The Vedas declare that Brahman is *Atman*, where Atman is the individual soul. You are Atman, which means that your soul is woven into the fabric of existence. But a soul isn't the same as a person, and the Vedas round out the picture by declaring, "Brahman is Atman, and Atman is *Jiva*," where Jiva is the individual person. (An analogy from the Upanishads is easier to grasp: Two birds are sitting in a tree. One eats while the other lovingly looks on. In this image Jiva is the bird eating the fruit, while its mate who looks on is Atman.)

"Brahman is Atman, and Atman is Jiva" gives your existence a cosmic dimension. In three Sanskrit words we embrace what medieval Christianity called the Great Chain of Being, an unbroken creation reaching from God down to the smallest particle in the quantum field. Because of the Great Chain of Being, God can see the fall of a sparrow. Yet somehow the Vedas, or any other wisdom tradition, didn't transform the people who listened to them. Then, as now, enlightenment bore little resemblance to everyday life. If your child gets sick or your water pipes burst in winter, an enlightened seer is the wrong person to go to. All you will hear is "Brahman is Atman, and Atman is Jiva," which seems like no help at all, under the circumstances.

This illustrates why we live in a topsy-turvy world. Instead of seeing life from the highest vision of possibilities, we see it from the level of mundane, everyday events. The intent of this book has been to turn the picture right side up. If you view your life from the highest vision first, you will still take a sick child to the doctor and call a plumber when your pipes burst in winter. But those events will be woven into the greater vision.

In other words, once you know your essence, you can seek the connection point between you (Jiva) and your true self or soul (Atman). The reason for making this connection is to experience the flow of love, compassion, insight, empathy, truth, beauty, creativity, and inner growth.

You are familiar by now with the eternal reality of these higher values—no one invented or imagined them. They are innate. They come packaged in human awareness at the source. Unfortunately, this aspect of "Brahman is Atman, and Atman is Jiva" got sidetracked when those words were disconnected from everyday life and relegated to spirituality only. In a similar way, Jesus's teaching, "The Kingdom of Heaven is within," was neglected when people decided that Heaven was outside themselves, a place above the clouds that can be reached only after we die.

When the most fundamental teachings about existence get diverted, it is inevitable that the world becomes topsy-turvy. The essence gets hidden under the chaotic welter of everyday duties, demands, and desires. A diamond is buried in the dust of the road. The poet William Wordsworth stated how things stood two hundred years ago: "The world is too much with us; late and soon. Getting and spending, we lay waste our powers."

Everything gets restored to what it should be when you are connected to your true self. In Vedic terms, Jiva cannot do without Atman. Higher consciousness isn't a goal. It is a hidden dimension. You cannot get there using your mind, your five senses, and your ego. But this isn't a counsel of despair. Your true self is made of awareness and nothing else. That's why it is valuable to become more aware, to do all you can to escape your unconscious habits, beliefs, and conditioning.

Yet there is a higher vision even than this, which sees everything not in consciousness but in existence. The hidden dimension, it turns out, requires no seeking. It requires only one thing: Be here now. This isn't a coded mystical message. It means what it says. If you are here now, that's enough. Instead of seeking your true self, it will find you wherever you are. There was a vexing problem that stirred the conscience of Victorian Christians. Will people living in faraway lands (in other words, heathens) be redeemed if they had never heard of Jesus? The answer was no, and it gave the impetus for the missionary work that spread around the world and continues today.

If you rephrase the question—"Will anyone find their

true self if they have never heard of it?"—the answer is yes. You cannot break the bond between Jiva and Atman. Only at the Jiva level (your individual "I") does ignorance exist. Atman knows you in the light of pure awareness. It is intimately in contact with your thoughts, words, and actions. Therefore, it and not you unfolds the path to the true self. By comparison, when a compass needle moves, it doesn't actually do anything. The attraction of the Earth's magnetic pole is in charge. It governs what the needle seems to be doing on its own.

The magnetic pull of the true self (known in Sanskrit as *swarupa*) is constantly operating, and you are constantly responding, even if you have never heard of the true self. Everything takes place in consciousness, following certain principles, as follows.

## How Your True Self Reaches You

Everyone can discern that their thoughts are always on the move, but what remains hidden is that everyone's state of awareness is also on the move. The tide of awareness creeps in and out like the ocean tides. Because the tide of awareness is always in flux, you can never be totally unaware. *Swarupa*, the pull of the self, is raising your state of awareness through the following means.

- The attraction of bliss. The mind is naturally pulled toward greater bliss.
- The experience of love. As the great Bengali poet Rabindranath Tagore affirmed, "Love is not a mere sentiment. It is the ultimate truth that lies at the heart of creation."
- The sudden appearance of an "aha" moment.
- The inspiration for great art, music, and poetry.
- The phenomenon of the peak experience, which reveals a vision of higher possibilities.
- The tradition of wisdom handed down over the centuries in every culture.
- The craving for meaning and purpose.
- The pull of curiosity and discovery.
- A vague sense that there is something more to life.
- The inner sense that you matter and are not alone.
- The inescapable feeling that there is a higher purpose behind everything.
- The urge for inner growth.
- Experiencing an intuition that turns out to be right.

These things are not equally distributed—one person experiences more of one thing and less of another. Sadly, there are people who suffer by being stranded in a state of anxiety, depression, and hopelessness. Even at low tide, however, awareness must move. The faintest glimmer of self-awareness can spark a new direction in someone's life.

The essential point is that the true self, although silent, is merged into everyone's life and has an influence. *Swarupa* is built into our design as human beings.

Does *Be here now* mean that there is nothing to do? That's a personal choice. Each one of us decides how much we want to grow, evolve, find meaning in our lives, and aspire to a higher state of consciousness. In many ways, the urgent problems facing humankind won't be solved without people who want all these things. Human beings evolve one person at a time.

## Simple awareness

The true significance of *Be here now* is trust. You can trust that existence contains not just the possibility but the reality of an ideal life. Existence isn't a blank slate—it is dynamic, blissful, and filled with untold possibilities. To realize this fully, you can begin practicing simple awareness. Simple awareness is a state that feels relaxed, open, and receptive. Most people feel the very opposite much of the time, thanks to ingrained habits that close the mind, the impact of stress that causes tension, and a fear of change, which makes the mind unreceptive.

Instead of trying to correct every problem head-on, simple awareness effortlessly lets the true self offer a solution. An important element is to remain centered during the day because this encourages your awareness to settle into a relaxed default. We presented a centering meditation on page 68 that will remind you of how the practice works. You possess a natural inner resilience that can be restored, until over time simple awareness will replace what most people experience as their default—being stressed and distracted.

Another aspect of simple awareness is that you start to connect with the subtle level of feeling. It is subtler to feel love than to feel fear; compassion is subtler than selfishness.

The common element in all subtle feelings is that they are blissful. The sweetness of life is imparted, needing nothing but to be here now. Subtle feeling is part of your design.

You can immediately begin to take advantage of this. Whenever you are faced with a situation that makes you feel confused, conflicted, or indecisive, pause for a moment. Quiet the dialogue going on in your mind and relax. Wait to sense how you really feel and what you need to do. For some people it helps to put their attention on their hearts or on the abdomen where "gut feelings" arise.

You aren't called on to suddenly seize a subtle inner impulse. The messages that people get "in here" are mixed. If you don't feel a clear guidance, just accept that and move on. The purpose, at the outset, is simply to turn inward. In time you will begin to recognize the calm, quiet, centered state of simple awareness where intuition and subtle feelings originate. This place is the opposite of where gross feelings come from, meaning

Anger, hostility

Resentment

Suspicion

Self-judgment

Anxiety

Fear

Remorse

Guilt

Shame

Selfishness

Envy and jealousy

A pattern of gross feelings drives everyone, so getting to a better level of awareness is invaluable. It isn't possible to fight against gross feelings once they arise. Those feelings are generated by the ego and its complete reliance on past experiences. Gross feelings repeat the past, leaving no room for subtler, truer messages, which come from the present. This distinction tells you not to trust your gross feelings. Even if you can't tune in to better messages, step away from the situation. Being aroused by gross feelings leads to bad decision-making and wrong choices you will later regret.

The choice that faces you now is how often and when to return to simple awareness. Don't let stressful moments overwhelm you; don't wait until you are overwhelmed. Simple awareness needs to become a project. It cannot be overemphasized that making simple awareness your default is effortless once you recognize what it feels like. After that, returning to it again and again brings your true self ever closer.

## Detachment

Finally, there is an aspect of *Be here now* that confuses almost everyone; namely, detachment. It concerns how and why to let go. The ego's insecurity makes clinging a constant temptation. Therefore, people tend to hold on a lot of the time and find it difficult to let go. We fear that letting go in a relationship, for example, will leave us lonely, unloved, and ignored. We fear letting go of comfortable beliefs and attitudes because we think they define us. Clinging is the opposite of trusting in existence.

Detachment calls on you to relinquish your attachment to whatever you want out of life. This doesn't mean you give up the intention to fulfill your desires—you just give up clinging to the outcome. Untold pain and suffering are rooted in the stubborn insistence that things must happen in one set way. This attitude gives rise to stuck-ness in many areas, including relationships, family, and career.

The more stuck you are, the more your ego clings, insisting that only one way is the right way. This insistence comes from the ego's fundamental insecurity. Its insecurity is inescapable. The alternative is to seek the guidance of deeper awareness; in other words, your true self. At this level you won't cling or get stuck.

The shift from clinging to detachment is so profound that it involves your very identity. If you identify with the chaotic bundle of experiences you call your life story, you are clinging to an illusion of who you are. The present moment isn't a story. It is a creative opportunity. Let new possibilities flow, and you gain the reward of detachment. In everyday usage *detachment* is misunderstood as "indifference." The two aren't the same. Indifference is the ego's attitude of "This has nothing to do with me." Detachment, on the other hand, involves an attitude of "I am open to whatever comes my way." Detachment allows you to live from a place where creative intelligence flows freely, without expectations or resistance, from your true self.

This is a very quiet, intimate thing. Nothing is more

personal than the fulfillment that comes from being your true self. Being here now might seem like no great thing. Everyone, after all, exists. But not everyone has attained the realization that existence is their crowning glory. The secret, like all the best mysteries, lies in plain sight. There is untold joy in knowing this and acting on it.

# PART FOUR

# The New Science of Life: Quantum Answers to Old Riddles

# Taking a Fresh Look

I n this section we take a deep dive into how the quantum body applies to the future of medicine. Although it is opening up rapidly, the whole field is still in its infancy. The quantum field lies at the horizon of matter and energy, including the materials that make up a cell and the energy it requires to stay alive. Cutting-edge concepts are being tested, with the most advanced data-collection techniques, to determine how the human body operates at the finest level, far finer than cells and organic molecules. The quantum revolution in physics is well over a century old, but connecting its key concepts to medicine was of minimal interest.

Medicine and physics were kept apart, first, because both fields are so specialized. A physicist working at a

high-speed particle accelerator views Nature through a
lens unknown to a heart surgeon. What made a new alli-
ance possible was the discovery that disease and aging
must be pursued even beyond the genome. DNA plays a
shadowy role in both. Sealed away in the nucleus of a cell,
your genes are protected from outside influences, or so it
was thought for decades.

Now we know that lifestyle choices and everyday experiences create changes, not in the genes you were born
with, but in genetic activity itself. Identical twins are born
with the same genes, yet they go through life having different experiences. By age seventy, the genetic profile of twins
is no closer than that of any two siblings born with family
genes but not identical ones. Moreover, life experiences
can be genetically passed down to future generations. If
your great-great-grandparents suffered through a famine,
markers of that trauma were probably left in their epigene
(the sheath of proteins surrounding DNA that governs genetic activity) and got passed down to their descendants.

The notion of a dynamic genome keeping a diary, as it
were, of every important life event that the body goes
through has opened the way for other discoveries. As we
noted earlier, medical research enjoyed a major breakthrough over the past decade when two factors were iso-

lated that link almost every major disorder: inflammation and stress. Inflammation was long known as a paradoxical process in the body. Disease and injured tissues need the added supply of oxygen and immune cells to heal that the inflammation response delivers. But, taken too far, as in the case of severe burns, inflammation can lead to shock and even death.

Stress is more clear-cut, since it has always been associated with harmful effects in the body and is linked to many disorders, from depression and anxiety to hypertension and lowered immunity. But a breakthrough occurred when it was suddenly realized that the culprits in disease and aging were not acute, dramatic instances of inflammation and stress. Instead, the damage to the body is low-level and steady, a chronic condition that does its damage slowly at the cellular level. It turns out that aging and chronic disease begin almost invisibly at the cellular level long before any symptoms appear, over a span of years or, most likely, decades.

Inflammation and stress are therefore a major focus in the deep dive we invite you to join in the following pages. Both are entwined in quantum-level processes inside every cell, and only quantum-level thinking can take us there. We will put the science in everyday language, because it is crucial for everyone, not just cell biologists and quantum physicists, to grasp the importance of crossing this new threshold. What lies ahead is fascinating, but even more exciting is the prospect of a new science of life that will unravel the medical mysteries that still confront us.

# Is Quantum Metabolism the Key to Disease and Aging?

The most important advances in science require new thinking, which is also true of personal breakthroughs. In the field of medical science, new treatments and research studies emerge at a bewildering rate. But the possibility of a major shift in thinking is rare, and the kind of revolution known as a "paradigm shift," which rethinks the entire model of the human body, is even rarer.

This is where modern physics enters the picture. At the quantum level, far deeper than medical research has explored, there is an exchange of energy, which is broadly classified as metabolism, from the Greek word *metabolē*, meaning "change." The change involves energy that every cell needs to sustain itself. You might think that this is simply like stoking a furnace with coal, but that's not the case.

There are many mysteries about metabolism that require a quantum explanation.

- How do cells know how much energy they need?
- How do cells communicate with each other to balance their energy needs and synchronize with one another?
- What's the secret of the complex molecular machinery that regulates everything happening in a cell?
- Where is the timer or clock that moves energy through every phase in our bodies from sleep to waking to vigorous activity?

These turn out to be quantum questions for the simple reason that chemistry and biology can't solve them using the time-honored metaphor of the body-as-machine. At the basis of the laws governing energy is entropy, the tendency for heat to move from a hotter place to a colder one. Entropy is why a mother says, "Eat your dinner before it gets cold," and why all the heat from the stars is being constantly dissipated in the cold void of space, where the temperature is near absolute zero.

The greatest mystery about metabolic energy, however,

is negative entropy, the state where heat builds up, rather than flowing away, and the human body is a miracle at doing this. Metabolism is a process of renewing every cell's energy supply, not just offsetting the heat our bodies give off, but trapping energy to deploy it, not simply to keep us warm, but to accomplish the amazing processes behind hearing, seeing, and thinking.

To give you a sense of just how miraculous negative entropy is, consider something as simple as the speed of energy moving from a warmer to a colder place. It is this that creates the arrow of time, which dictates that time moves forward and cannot be reversed to move backward. In a static universe, entropy might be so slow that change occurs too gradually to create the passage of time. Our universe is so dynamic that time and entropy are intimately linked, which is also true of our bodies.

In scientific terminology, "nanoscale molecular motors" drive the efficient energy transfer in all cells. Inflammation and stress may distort energy transfer, making it proceed more slowly than normal; this causes the warmth and red skin associated with an inflamed wound or infection. The chronic stress response is the fundamental basis for the amplification of all chronic disease states. Depression is most often rooted in stress-generated anxiety, for example, along with the degraded processes that cause chronic disease.

At their core, anxiety and depression, which massively drain a person's energy and vitality for life, are inextricably linked. They inherently drive the chronic stress response. From this perspective chronic diseases are metabolic disorders, whatever the specific medical diagnosis might be (obesity, type 2 diabetes, hypertension, etc.). Accordingly, the evolutionary fight-or-flight response stops being short-term in emergencies and becomes long-term in our metabolism.

The linchpin is that efficient biological energy production is impaired and deteriorates over time in critical parts of the cell. For optimal health, the flow of energy across metabolic pathways must be efficiently transformed into useful work. In other words, the entire system processes energy in an organized, coherent, and purposeful way. It's the exact opposite of a bonfire throwing heat off in all directions randomly and without purpose.

Physics, to turn to a more technical explanation, would say that inflammation is like the "de-coherence of quantum physical systems." In layman's terms, the tiny quantum motors that drive metabolism must remain orderly and connected. Quantum processes level the playing field for everything, not just for our cells but for hundreds of biological clocks, thousands of chemical reactions per second, hormonal cycles, and the life cycles of the microorganisms known as the "microbiome." The recent Nobel Prize awarded for the discovery of the molecular clocks embedded in all our cells emphasizes the importance of living in harmony with the circadian cycles of the Earth. They synchronize all those tiny cellular timekeepers.

At that point a complex new horizon appears, known as the "fitness landscape." In evolutionary terms, some species thrive and evolve while others reach a dead end and remain the same or become extinct. Darwin's theory of evolution broke this down into two factors—getting enough food to survive and finding a mate to reproduce and carry on the species.

But modern evolutionary biology deals in what is happening at the level of genes, because, ultimately, survival is a genetic process. Your own genes are affected by every experience you and your ancestors have ever had. The same is true of every species, so a fitness landscape attempts mathematically to envision every factor that might create changes in genes over time.

Imagine a saber-toothed tiger faced with stresses in its environment and meeting those stresses within the animal's range of metabolic controls and regulation. If a condition appears that the tiger's genes cannot adapt to (known technically as a "bifurcation point"), disaster awaits. In our bodies a major bifurcation occurs between being healthy and being sick and aging. Enter the field of quantum metabolism, which deals with the finest level where energy is supplied and used by a cell. It provides the rules of the road that quantum motors follow, which leads, using elegant mathematics, to why rules of energy transfer are being violated when metabolic inefficiency appears, leading to disease and aging.

It turns out that the most important metabolic parameters of the human body are redox (the rise and fall of oxidation rates), free energy, and acid-base balance. These factors are maintained in a narrow physiological range in healthy states. The deterioration from health to disease involves stress pushing these key metabolic parameters out of their narrow ranges of stability. There are many ways that the deterioration might start—in something as basic, chemically speaking, as oxidation rates. A small, localized imbalance can eventually bring down the whole body, exemplifying the old adage "For want of a nail, the kingdom was lost."

The common thread in this complex train of investigation is this: Physiological fitness declines as energy is lost from the system. This results in the degradation of structure and function in cells and the body as a whole. These are changes of state, not simply linear processes moving from A to B. Specific events can trigger a change of state, just as a broken hip in the elderly can lead to death, even though breaking a hip isn't considered fatal in itself.

Quantum processes determine, regulate, and control changes of state, so understanding them can allow us to forestall disease and aging at the deepest level. Aging in terms of symptoms is personal, unique, and unpredictable. Quantum processes aren't. A much-needed foundation is provided akin to how DNA and gene mapping gave a foundation to evolution and inheritance.

Because it triggers disorder in a cascade through molecules, cells, tissues, organs, and the whole body, stress is critical in the fitness landscape human beings occupy, along with all other living creatures. Stress response, when viewed technically, is a measure that can be quantified for a person's, or a species's, evolving physiological fitness.

In human physiology, unpredictable changes in the course of a disease might arise due to an astonishing complexity of molecular interactions. Even modern physics finds itself challenged by this complexity. If we are to reach the cherished goal of a truly precise medicine, massive amounts of data are being accumulated by genomics (the mapping of genomes), metabolomics (the study of small molecules produced by energy-transformation processes in cells), and proteomics (the study of proteins in systems and organs), allowing us to rely on computers and artificial intelligence to clarify the essential things we need to know. The human body is literally being reinvented before our eyes. Insights from modern physics are needed to realize the full potential of this emerging paradigm shift. Yet, without a doubt, it is proceeding and accelerating every day.

# What If Aging Is a Mistake?

Since no one wants to age, there is a tremendous incentive to prevent, slow down, or even reverse the aging process. But all these efforts run into the same obstacle. No one actually knows what aging is or precisely what causes it. On its face, this riddle shouldn't exist. The universe is subject to ever-increasing entropy, which causes everything, including the universe itself, to run down like a child's toy whose battery is slowly drained. Biology chimes in with the obvious fact that all higher living things grow old and die.

But reality changes depending on your viewpoint, and one viewpoint tells us that aging—especially human aging—might be a mistake. First, we need to counter the evidence that living things must grow old and die. This is

more easily done than you might suppose. Here's a thumbnail sketch of the counterargument against aging:

- Entropy refers to the dissipation of heat by
  which warm things grow colder. But those are
  inanimate things. Life preserves and increases
  energy. Putting on a coat in winter effectively
  defeats entropy, and so have all living forms for
  at least 4 billion years.
- The universe may die a "heat death" as it
  approaches absolute zero, but, in the meantime,
  complex forms keep arising and surviving. The
  force that creates them is evolution.
- Unique among the living things yet discovered,
  *Homo sapiens* can consciously choose to evolve.
- Long ago *Homo sapiens* escaped the prison of
  Darwinian survival of the fittest by moving in
  any direction that offers more complexity,
  creativity, and discovery.

As you can see, these are fundamental facts that can be
used to approach aging, making it far from inevitable. An
ancient Indian scripture declares, "People grow old and die
because they see other people grow old and die."
  What if this were literally true—that we age by being

conditioned to age? Partial proof is offered by lifestyle. Two generations ago, no one took seriously the prevention of heart disease, hypertension, recovery from stroke, and the advantages of pure food, water, and air. Now all these things are common knowledge, and life expectancy has continued to rise. Even more critical, the span of wellness has extended into old age, and many people in developed countries may achieve something unknown to the human race for thousands of years: wellness that lasts a lifetime.

So far, so good—the anti-aging camp has some scientific facts on our side as well as proof that life span can be extended. Nor are we beyond the notion that people grow old and die because they see other people grow old and die. This position turns aging into a failure of consciousness by which old habits and conditioning block true awareness.

Your state of awareness fundamentally influences how and why you age. Here are some striking examples:

- Recent research indicates that people suffering from extreme grief are prone to a quicker death.
- At the cellular level, one theory of aging says that levels of a protein known as telomerase correlate with how long a cell lives and how much DNA wears down with time. Research has shown that even a short period of practicing

meditation increased telomerase levels by
40 percent.

- Stress accelerates aging. Caregivers who spend
all day with Alzheimer's patients have shown
a tendency to shorten their life spans by 5 to
8 years.

These are illuminating facts, but to tackle aging directly, we must dig deeper. Your body is organized on time schedules that are many and complex. Biorhythms regulated by biological clocks span from a scale of a few thousandths of a second for the swirling chemical reactions in every cell to an entire lifetime.

When biorhythms get out of sync, entropy speeds up and aging accelerates. One can spend a lifetime as a medical researcher studying just hormones, key players in the ebb and flow of every bodily process, including hunger, sex, mood, growth, and sleep. But in everyday life one can cut to the chase. Biological clocks are designed to remain in sync unless interfered with. What interferes with them is stress, poor-quality sleep, overwork, and overstimulation of the central nervous system caused by constant noise, distraction, and everyday pressures at home and at work.

To ultimately solve the mystery of aging, however, we need to probe into the very heart of Nature. Nature coordinates every level of matter, energy, time, and space. These parameters can expand and contract because relativity governs them and links them together. Entropy relates to the arrow of time because events in the macro or larger world aren't reversible. If you break a glass, the arrow of time dictates that you cannot unbreak it again and make it whole.

However, as you get down to finer and finer levels of Nature, reality becomes peculiar. The basic forces of Nature, such as electromagnetism and gravity, exist without regard to time. Reverse time, standard time, and no time are all possible. In some astonishing way, totally outside present knowledge, the quantum world of reverse time and no time meshes perfectly with the macro world governed by the arrow of time.

What invisible force could account for this? There is no known physical force. However, one element of human existence meshes with no time, reverse time, and standard time: consciousness. In memory we return to the past; in imagination we fly into the future. Time hangs heavy and moves slowly if you are depressed; time speeds up and is light as a feather when you fall in love.

In deep meditation, yogis use consciousness alone to radically slow down bodily processes. A standard demonstration of yogic powers involves burying a *sadhu*, or holy man, in a box underground. With nothing but the air in the box to sustain him, a yogi can slow his heart rate and breathing to the extent that he will emerge from burial a week later perfectly alive and healthy.

Let's call this example the zero point of aging, since it is close to the zero point of physiology. At the quantum level, there is also a zero point at the horizon before space, time, matter, and energy emerge to create the known universe. What if a yogi's zero point and Nature's zero point are the same, or at least analogous? There was a time when physics knew nothing about the quantum world, and, as a result, a host of calculations were wrong or could not be made. This is the crux of anti-aging today. In the absence of the kind of knowledge possessed by Yoga, we make wrong calculations about our bodies and miss out on calculations yet to be discovered.

Every scientific model has its blind spots, and for many decades consciousness has been the major blind spot of mainstream science. But as we have just discussed, science is expansive enough to provide a model that not only includes consciousness but traces it to the quantum level of Nature. The brain is likely to be a quantum device that we are using very clumsily. Higher consciousness is likely to be nothing more than a state where the brain is called on to modify its workings in such a way that it gives quantum information to every cell in the body, being directed from the zero point of consciousness where time itself is controlled.

A hundred years ago, such a proposition would have been insanity. Fifty years ago, it was the remotest of possibilities. Today it is an exciting probability with the trend of evidence moving rapidly in the right direction. If the mistake of aging is ever to be corrected, this is the course we must follow.

# Why Isn't Your Body Perfect?

From everything science tells us about elementary particles, there is no good reason that the human body shouldn't be perfect. The scientific model builds Nature up from the simplest, smallest components to the largest and most complex. There is no doubt that, at the smallest scale, subatomic particles, atoms, and molecules are perfect because they have endured without change for billions of years.

Did imperfections arise with the beginning of life on Earth? Single-cell microorganisms are thousands, perhaps millions, of times larger and more complex than the smallest molecules that they are built from. But one-celled creatures have endured for something like 3.5 billion years. Since they reproduce by cell division, the most ancient forms of amoebas, algae, protists, and so on are actually still with us—literally the first amoeba has never died or aged. Life-forms with complex structures constitute much less than 1 percent of living things; a bucket of ocean water is likely to contain hundreds of unknown variations on their DNA.

Imperfection gained the stage thanks to the same force that produced perfection: evolution. We suffer from disease, resist aging, and fear death, but all of these are creative steps as far as evolution is concerned, since evolution triumphs through maximum diversity and an endless supply of new genes leading to improvements and adaptations.

What evolution needs isn't necessarily what humans desire. From the moment that early hominids started taking care of the weak, elderly, and sick (not that a specific date is known), our species defied survival of the fittest. Now modern people are the weakest animals in our infant state, needing a long childhood and adolescence to become fully developed. We are saddled with bodies that display incredible efficiency to stay alive, even though amoebas and algae leave us in the dust, but the gross imperfections of sickness, aging, and death remain with us.

To get past these obstacles, what is needed—more and better science, the healthiest possible lifestyle, genetically based wonder drugs? Our view is that these are important advances, but they don't get to the heart of the problem. The heart of the problem is that science hasn't told us what the human body actually is. Let us sketch in what our bodies do that remains mysterious and often unfathomable.

- *Energy management.* Living beings fight against energy loss, or entropy, by using the energy stored in food. Raw energy becomes diversified in every cell, some of it used for building proteins, keeping the cell's rigid structure, its "bones and muscles" intact, reproducing through cell division, repelling invaders, eliminating waste, and much more. No human-made machinery is nearly this efficient or diverse.

- *Balance.* The human body is subject to much more stress than any other living creature because we live lives filled with noise, accidents, violence, pressures at work, and difficult relationships while also pushing ourselves to perform extreme physical feats, like climbing mountains and running a marathon. In the face of these stresses, our bodies can withstand only a narrow temperature range—a fever higher than four or five degrees Fahrenheit can lead to permanent brain damage or death. Yet somehow our bodies remain in dynamic balance and can return to a resting state as soon as external stresses are removed or lessened.

- *Coherence.* The ability of one system to sync with another is essential to life. Atoms, molecules, cells, tissues, and organs must cooperate in a single living community. How they do this remains a total mystery. Physics might introduce quantum coherence and electromagnetic fields, but these are rudimentary concepts when it comes to creating and maintaining the human body, or even a single cell.

- *Asymmetry.* Balance and coherence are totally necessary for living things, but they also spell its death knell without imbalance and incoherence. Nature breaks eggs to make omelets through a process known to physicists as "symmetry breaking." Instead of remaining balanced and intact, the dynamic processes in the body need a perfectly regulated mix of creation and destruction. How these opposites coexist remains mysterious.

To keep things simple, we'll stop there. Life is explored through other models such as information theory, thermodynamics, and quantum biology that make advances every year. But, at bottom, imperfection exists not on the physical plane or even in the domain of information. The root of imperfection is an imperfect model of the body to begin with. We'll sketch the most glaring flaws as follows:

- *The body-as-machine.* The scientific consensus is that the human body is an incredibly complex machine, yet it isn't machinelike at all. Machines can't heal themselves, think, have mood swings, feel happy or sad, and so on. All machines wear out over time through friction and entropy. But if you exercise, your muscles improve with use, and cells repair themselves with self-generated processes totally foreign to a machine.

- *The body-as-thing.* Get even more basic than the machine model, and you arrive at the notion that the body is a physical object that displays the characteristics common to rocks, mountains, and stars. Yet the thingness of the body is undermined by the fact that none of its building blocks are alive, and no one knows how inanimate matter learned to live, much less think, feel, and become self-aware.

- *A miracle of complexity.* Looking at the human brain's 100 billion neurons and quadrillion synaptic connections, surely, we are the product of complexity, beginning with the structure of DNA. But complexity cannot explain how the mind was created. As someone wittily said, relating the mind to complex biochemicals is like saying that if you add more cards to a deck of playing cards, the deck of cards will learn how to play poker.

- *Information storehouse.* The current fad for information theory rests on two things: first, the obvious fact that systems at every level of Nature must "remember" the information encoded in them, and, second, that information seems to get us out of the bind with physical things and their inability to be alive. Information keeps knowledge intact outside the limits of physicality. Still, the most educated mind, stuffed with decades of information gathering, doesn't protect the body from getting sick, aging, and dying.

Since all these models are fatally flawed, what model is better? One based on consciousness. Mind can't be created from the nuts and bolts of the physical universe. We are conscious beings first and foremost. Therefore, why not start with consciousness as the essential ingredient, the X factor that explains how our own complex lives arose? Once science begins to explore Nature as a flow of creative intelligence, many mysteries disappear overnight and new horizons open. The fact that boundaries are breaking down already is the surest sign we have that the imperfection of the human body will be revealed as needless and open to change.

# A New Angle:
## The Fitness Landscape

t has been well established that the afflictions of the elderly are chronic conditions like type 2 diabetes, hypertension, coronary artery disease, and probably most cancers, which begin to develop years or even decades before symptoms appear.

A piecemeal approach, taking one disorder at a time, doesn't match how the body works, which is as a field—that's the basic concept behind the quantum body. But we can bring the field closer to everyday life using no scientific jargon at all.

Let's begins with a visual image. Visualize a valley surrounded by mountains. You live in the valley, but your livelihood (perhaps you are a woodcutter or forest ranger) takes you up the mountain, and when your labor is done, you come back down to resume your life in the valley.

This image forms the basis of the "fitness landscape," as the new model is known. The landscape consists of a valley (your normal healthy state) while the mountains are the stresses and challenges your body withstands from disease, trauma, anxiety, depression, and aging. The promise of lifelong wellness lies in your ability to climb up the "mountain" of these challenges and then to return to the "valley" of normal good health.

Younger people make this trip quickly, which gives them a steep slope from valley to mountain, and the valley they return to is the same as the one they left. (In some models the visual image of youth climbs to higher and higher valleys, which represent increasing states of well-being.) But in the face of aging, traumas, stress, and disease, it gets harder to climb the mountain and return home to the valley of a healthy mind and body. Time works against us. If you make little or no effort to make the journey, things grow worse. Like a weak spring that refuses to snap back into place except slowly and weakly, inertia (both physical and mental) saps your resilience. Bouncing back becomes harder.

There is a second aspect to the fitness landscape that brings another insight. When you go to the doctor and have various vital signs measured, the readout of your tests gives a snapshot of things like blood pressure, heart rate, blood sugar, etc. But the body is constantly on the move and so are these vital signs. A single test is like taking a snapshot of a moving target. Your blood pressure today is just a single point when what you need are lines on a map to show you where you are going. If the trajectory of your blood pressure, cholesterol, blood oxygen, and so on is known, you will be able to see a trend, and the trend is what really matters, not the snapshots.

The landscape of fitness goes beyond the normal use of the word *fitness*, which conveys images of the gym and keeping your muscles toned. As beneficial as that might be, we are talking about something holistic. Your whole body-mind needs to be fit so that you can easily make the effort to go up the mountain in full confidence that you will return to the valley again. The danger is that you will not make it back to the same valley but will tumble into another valley, thus creating for yourself a new baseline. In this valley you adapt to a new normal that cannot be easily reversed, such as chronic hypertension, depression, anxiety, obesity, or permanent deficits from disease and aging.

*Holistic* tends to sound abstract and beyond normal understanding, so let's substitute *personal*. Your state of well-being is nothing if not personal, and this is in keeping with the fitness landscape we are talking about. Your wellness profile embraces everything, from your psychological mood to your satisfaction at work, your general health and past medical history, your relationships, and your time of life. Medical science cannot guide you optimally through these interconnected factors, yet somehow you must find a way to navigate them successfully.

The best guideline is probably resilience. Resilience, like a strong spring that bounces back quickly, gives you the ability to climb up the mountain (whether it is getting sick, undergoing surgery, going through a divorce, having a baby, or any other challenge that involves stress) and return to the valley as good as new. "As good as new" is amazingly easy in youth, more challenging in middle age, and a cause for increased awareness over age sixty-five, but the point is always the same: Good as new is your standard or benchmark at any age.

Good as new is multidimensional. Love, joy, creativity, empathy, compassion, inner peace, and self-worth do not age. They are good as new at any time of life. Therefore, they should be the focus of your resilience. If you are always creative, your fitness landscape will benefit much more than from going to the gym and eating your quinoa. Speaking more broadly, the key to all the things we have just mentioned is awareness. Consciousness is where the ultimate resilience lies—physical, mental, emotional, and in your relationships.

The time is nearer than you think for wearables like watches, headbands, or even rings that will monitor the key vital signs that indicate your general state of health and resistance to stress, among other variables like heart rate and blood pressure. But the responsibility is yours to stay resilient in your awareness, keep "good as new" as your life-long goal, and make the effort to climb the mountain, confident that you will return home to the valley. The new model of the fitness landscape, based on positive motivations instead of fearful risks, is exciting enough to open a new future for everyone.

# The Remarkable Importance
## of the Goldilocks Zone

I n the search for life on other planets, a concept known as the "Goldilocks zone" is critical. This is the region, not too close to a star but also not too far away, that makes the development of life possible. The critical factor is heat, since being too close to a star, as Mercury and Venus are in our solar system, is intolerably hot, while being too far away, as Saturn and Jupiter are, is intolerably cold. The Goldilocks zone makes sense, although there has to be a fudge factor, since large enough planets and moons can generate their own heat.

Yet simple as it sounds, the Goldilocks zone determines in many ways how successful someone's life will be and at the same time the likelihood of enjoying wellness to age seventy and beyond. The human Goldilocks zone begins with our physiology. The human body has a surprisingly narrow range of temperature for survival—it is life-threatening to have a fever over 105°F or hypothermia below 95°F for a sustained amount of time. Our Goldilocks zone for internal temperature is therefore only 10°F.

But your body has many overlapping Goldilocks zones. For example, it can be fatal to go without water for 3 days, without sleep for 11 days (the longest anyone has remained awake—sleep deprivation causes damage long before that), and without oxygen to the brain for 3 minutes. Then there are our Goldilocks zones that apply to psychology. If someone is lonely, depressed, anxious, grieving, or under stress beyond a certain limit, there is a point of no return that leads to a chronic condition, and the effects can spread to the body as well—the chronically depressed, for example, are at greater risk for disease and premature death.

Complex as this picture is—and we've barely scratched the surface—lifelong well-being seems to depend on something simple: staying inside your Goldilocks zones. This small piece of advice actually links many phenomena that are confirmed by medicine, psychology, and the social sciences. Here's a partial list.

- Inflammation has been linked to a wide range of chronic disorders, including hypertension, heart disease, and probably cancer. It takes only a low level of chronic inflammation, not even noticeable to the patient, to throw off the body's efficient distribution of heat. A cascading effect then begins, leading to cellular disturbances and eventually disease symptoms.

- Stress affects every system in the body, as well as our emotions. The stress response evolved to deal with acute stress lasting a few minutes or hours, but a low-level stress response that is triggered by constant pressures at work or in relationships, for example, initiates the negative side of the stress response. The first signs are psychological, typically beginning with dullness and lethargy, but over time they expand to the physical, affecting practically everything regulated by the nervous and endocrine (hormone) system.

- As part of our species's need for survival, social bonds developed that are necessary for groups if they want to get enough food, ward off predators, and control the threat of violence from possible invaders. The Goldilocks zone in this case is about support and bonding. If you are isolated, lonely, and cut off from social support (particularly close friends and family), your chances for success and well-being are seriously diminished.

These critical zones are intertwined, which is why, for example, someone who has few or no support systems in his or her life is at higher risk for a heart attack and a slower recovery, or even death, if a heart attack occurs. It is fascinating to see how basic principles from physics apply to creatures as complicated as *Homo sapiens.* In physics, subatomic particles are linked in a phenomenon known as quantum entanglement, while human beings have bodies in which every cell is entangled (interconnected) with every other, and we engage in relationships that bond us through emotional entanglement.

Nature is defined, in fact, as a hierarchy of connections, which is in keeping with an ancient axiom from India that can be roughly translated as "As is the great, so is the small. As is the atom, so is the universe." Similarly, in the West the hermetic axiom states, "As above, so below." We threaten our lives at every level by venturing too far outside the Goldilocks zones. Sleep, water, and body temperature have already been mentioned, but to expand the picture, we need to resort to the "broken-windows theory" from sociology. To disrupt a neighborhood, the theory goes, you only need to have a few broken windows that go without repair. The sight of such small cracks in social coherence leads to more incoherence. The house with the broken windows is subject to vandalism, for example, while the general appeal of the whole neighborhood is threatened, and standards of upkeep begin to unravel.

The validity of the broken-windows theory is debatable when it comes to society but not when it comes to our bodies. A single malignant cell can develop into a tumor, the tumor into metastasized cancer, and the cancer into a life-ending decline. Generally speaking, at the moment of death more than 99 percent of your DNA is likely to be functioning normally. It takes the breakdown of only a single vital organ or system (such as the heart or the respiratory system) to be fatal.

The simplest lesson from the broken-windows metaphor is not to let a window get broken in the first place. In terms of everyday existence, the window gets broken in mysterious ways when it comes down to why a single cell becomes malignant or an arterial lining cracks, leading to atherosclerosis (hardening of the arteries). Conditions as pervasive as type 1 diabetes and chronic hypertension also have obscure origins.

But the most essential factors across the board appear to be poor-quality sleep, inflammation, and stress, always remembering that they are linked. Priority must be given to good, sound sleep every night and lowering everyday stress, which is apparently a trigger for inflammatory processes at the cellular level. Ironically, as sound as the research is on these lifestyle factors, good sleep and stress reduction tend to be the last things people really pay attention to.

More broadly, once you have attended to these factors, there is the positive side of being in the Goldilocks zone. If you are emotionally resilient, self-reliant, motivated by a larger purpose in life, and feel secure in the support you receive from, and give to, others, you are actually respecting a different Goldilocks zone in each case. There is no more reliable guide than honoring ourselves while supporting the well-being of others when it comes to achieving lifelong wellness, success, and rewarding relationships.

# Why Creation Is Unthinkable

I n both worldviews—the Vedic and the quantum—
the goal is the same, to explain creation. Yet some
frustrating dead ends occur no matter what perspective
you take. The human brain puts up a wall that seems insur-
mountable. Unless the skull is opened in anatomy class or
surgery, we wouldn't even know we had a brain. But the
brain's blindness goes much deeper.

The most basic rule taught to journalism students is
known as the five Ws. A news story must answer five questions beginning with the letter W: Who?, What?, When?,
Where?, and Why?

If a bank on Main Street is held up by three known
bank robbers on Christmas Day, the five Ws are easy. But
these questions have proved nearly impossible when it
comes to the daily reality everyone is living. Quantum phys-

ics played a large part in blurring "Where?" and "When?"—at the quantum level; any event is merely a probability that has no defined edges in time and space. The quantum field itself has no location—it is everywhere at once.

"Who?" doesn't figure into quantum calculations, because the self isn't quantifiable into data, and science proceeds by using data. "Why?" is also dismissed, since science deals in the how of creation, not its purpose or meaning. This leaves us with only "What?," which in journalism school stands for "What happened?" Here, at least, the question is clear-cut and scientific. What happened (and continues to happen) is the process of creation, embracing the Big Bang on the largest scale and subatomic particles on the smallest.

It is frustrating for modern science that out of the five Ws, only one is answerable in a clear, rational way. The Vedic worldview, however, answers all five Ws. By now we've arrived at the point in this book where the Vedic answers are no longer incomprehensible.

*Who is the story about?* Human beings creating conscious experiences.

*What happened?* Creation emerged when pure consciousness began to manifest as an experience.

*When did it happen?* Before time began.

*Where did it happen?* In a location where space was created.

*Why did it happen?* Because it is in the nature of consciousness to create.

The frustrating problem with these answers isn't that they are wrong. In fact, they merge with quantum physics once physics allows for consciousness in the universe. Quantum body and causal body are synonyms, as we've seen. The problem is that both worldviews are attempting to describe something that is inconceivable. The human brain isn't up to the challenge through ordinary thinking.

Thinking happens in words (when it concerns scientific questions, at least), and words have already failed us in the five Ws, no matter which worldview you favor. Two answers are nonsensical.

*When did it happen?* Before time began.

This is nonsensical because *before* is a word based in linear time. The everyday world operates with clock time to measure before and after, yet wherever time came from, things don't operate that way. Otherwise, it would just be another version of time, not its creator.

*Where did it happen?* In a location where space was created.

This answer is nonsensical because *where* applies to places in space, not to the location where space was created.

Once you rule out "When?" and "Where?" the human brain is incapable of processing those questions. After all, it operates in spacetime. Everything your brain is composed of—mainly water and some basic elements like carbon, hydrogen, oxygen, and nitrogen—is trapped in space and time. They offer no escape route into a reality that goes beyond space and time, which is where creation begins.

In short, the brain doesn't have a clue about creation, even though it transmits creative ideas all the time. In a very mysterious way, everything you can conceive of—the most brilliant thought, the deepest emotion, the most beautiful art and music—comes from a source that is inconceivable. It is hard to bring this fact down to earth. An example or two might help.

A composer from Bach to the Beatles works with only a small handful of notes—counting the sharps and flats, there are only twelve notes in a standard Western scale. It is amazing to think that millions of compositions can be based on just twelve notes, and no one can explain how that is done. Composers don't use mathematical algorithms to create music. They aim for the beautiful, and if a melody like the Beatles' "Let It Be" emerges, millions of listeners immediately recognize its beauty. No one can say how this shared perception works, but if you turned "Let It Be" upside down on the music stand, listeners would instantly know that the beauty had vanished, replaced by something indifferent or even ugly.

It is inconceivable to understand why Mozart and Lennon-McCartney are great melodists while many famous composers like Beethoven aren't. Beautiful music is something you know when you hear it. This knowing exists in consciousness. There is no region in the brain that detects beauty.

The brain does many things that pose the same riddle. Possessing a cerebral cortex enabled you to learn arithmetic and Einstein to formulate the General Theory of Relativity. But we have the same higher brain as our prehistoric ancestors thirty thousand years ago, and they had no use for arithmetic. In all likelihood they couldn't even count their fingers and toes. Unused abilities naturally die out in a genetic pool. Being able to do math is an ability that reversed the rule, persisting before it was needed by thousands of years. Where does mathematics come from in the first place? The only reasonable answer is consciousness.

Gourmets delight in the taste of black truffles, and

there is no mystery to the chemical composition of this rare fungus that pigs snuffle out in French oak forests. But there is no explanation for what tastes good and what doesn't, or indeed why anything even has a taste in the first place. All five senses come from an inconceivable place, as do memory, love, truth, and the other qualities we experience and take for granted.

Clearly, the creative process isn't yielding up its mystery, even when it comes to the most basic aspects. Companies like Microsoft and Apple keep their market edge through creative innovation, and they have a lot at stake in the creativity of the people they hire. It would be invaluable to speed up the creative process or at least to figure out who is creative and why. Yet after much time, money, and effort, studies on creativity have concluded that creativity can't be sped up or imparted to those who aren't creative in the first place. Like the brain that doesn't know it exists, we create without knowing how or why.

Yet the nature of the inconceivable runs much deeper. This was acknowledged by an article in the January 2023 issue of *Scientific American* titled "The Universe Is Not Locally Real." Calling this "one of the more unsettling discoveries of the past half century" might be understating things, because looking past the language of quantum physics, what the article sets out to prove is that "local" (i.e., physical) objects do not have defined edges and boundaries, or even definite properties. They acquire these properties, such as weight, mass, location, etc., only when you stop to measure them. Or to go a step further, objects gain their realness by being perceived.

Einstein was skeptical about quantum mechanics because it led to the absurd conclusion that the moon (or any physical object) doesn't exist until you look at it. But that's the implication that now appears to be (almost) proven. Seeing is believing, we all will say, but seeing is actually creating, which makes no sense. Why should looking at an object, which seems totally passive, create its properties? Why should measuring the same object, without touching it in any way, create the property you are measuring?

What pertains to subatomic particles also pertains to the quantum body: It must also be created out of potentialities and possibilities. Creation begins in a field of infinite possibilities and unfolds in stages all the way up to the physical world. What makes your physical body real is the flow of possibilities through every level of creation. You stand at the pivot point of creation, because your body is defined by how you relate to it. This sounds just as strange as the notion in quantum theory that waves turn into particles by being observed. Yet once again Heisenberg offers a neat formulation of the truth: "What we observe is not nature itself, but nature exposed to our method of questioning."

As applied to your body, when you were an infant, you might have waved your hand in front of your eyes without knowing that it belonged to you. A hand was just a pale thing waving around in the air. Then you started asking questions:

What is this thing?

Does it belong to me?

How does it feel to have a hand?

What can a hand do?

From these basic questions, infinite possibilities started to reveal themselves as you grew in awareness. Can your hand whip up a soufflé, play Bach on the piano, catch a fly ball, or set a record playing a video game? The hand's potential is unlimited while the potential of the hand of a higher primate like a gorilla or chimpanzee isn't, because *you* can pose questions that explore infinite possibilities. Without you to experience it, a hand is still just a pale thing floating before your eyes.

If you have a body only by experiencing it, who is the experiencer? This question brings us back to the most mysterious of the five Ws—Who; namely, "Who is the story about?" Find a good answer, and you will find the very core of creation. If you have ever sat down and seriously asked, "Who am I?," you've done something few people ever do.

A profound choice to free yourself faces you. If you look down the road far enough, "Who am I?" leads all the way to Einstein's assertion that either nothing is a miracle or everything is. At first glance, there doesn't seem to be a connection between "I" and miracles. But a miracle, simply defined, is a supernatural event. *Super* is the Latin prefix for "over" or "above." That's precisely the issue with the mystery of "I." Does it point us to something above or beyond Nature?

You can't go beyond Nature using rational thinking, because the brain is bound up in the limits of space and time. But you can transcend raw Nature, meaning that you can determine the level of consciousness where your awareness is focused. Potential isn't the same as achievement, however, so it is possible to possess the potential for higher consciousness and still turn your back on it. It is the easiest thing in the world to remain ignorant of your status as a cosmic being. Here's how you do it:

Think the same way everyone else thinks.

Follow old habits and conditioning.

Accept society's collective beliefs.

Conform in order to remain safe.

Cling to your story as your identity.

Protect your self-image.

Look out for number one.

Once you see the situation for what it is, you are on the threshold of the solution, which lies in the axiom "Clear away your illusions, and what remains will be real." Contrary to everything you have accepted about your everyday self, you are already supernatural, meaning that your quantum body transcends the physical world. No struggle, journey, quest, or massive challenge is demanded. The minute you see how the illusion works, it starts to drop away.

Despite our flaws and blind spots, where humans want to go—when viewed over the span of centuries—is deeper and deeper into our own nature. The fact that we can use chemistry, physics, mathematics, and technology to get there shows how extensive those tools have become. Once you see your true source in consciousness, the rishis have done their job. You have arrived where true creativity begins. Who, what, where, when, and why all get answered. They are all you.

# How to Write Your Memories in Air

Memories are cherished or feared, depending on whether they are good or bad memories, so it makes sense to have as many happy experiences as possible. We can call this sound psychological advice, but spirituality is different. From the ancient Indian tradition comes a saying: "First experiences are written in stone, then in sand, then in water, and finally in air."

In this one sentence the path of enlightenment has been encapsulated, once you unravel what the sentence means. It concerns the ability of experiences to stick with us as memories. If a memory is so strong that it makes a deep, even lifelong impression, it is like words engraved in stone. To find freedom, to live in the present moment, you can't be bound up in the past, which is what strong, sticky, stubborn memories do. Therefore, the spiritual path isn't about getting as many positive memories as you can. It's about whether your memories are holding you back, over-shadowing the present with ghosts from the past.

The past is a mental illusion created by memories. The present moment is free from the past, and as we live in the moment more and more, your memories loosen their grip. As the Indian axiom says, they are no longer engraved in stone but are like writing in sand, then water, and finally air. If this sequence sounds mysterious, that's chiefly be-cause modern Western science hasn't solved the mystery of memory in the first place.

In functional terms, memory is the ability to record, store, and retrieve information. Using this definition, mag-nets "remember" to maintain their orientation, rubber re-members to snap back after being stretched, a heart cell remembers how to beat, and computers remember any-thing that can be coded digitally into bits consisting of ones and zeros. But human memory, while resembling all those things, is so mysterious that no explanation for it has ever been devised.

The mystery of human memory will be solved only when two other mysteries—time and the self—are solved. When Einstein revolutionized physics by introducing rel-ativity, time became flexible, and modern theories went on to make time reversible as well. Yet human experience had already done both things, and more. In memory we bring back the past in a kind of mental time travel that reverses clock time, which always moves forward.

But this provides a major clue about the deceptions created by memory, because no journey into the past is actually happening. Memories occur in the present. In terms of physiology this must be so because all cells, including the neurons in the memory centers of the brain, operate only in the present. We retrieve a memory by activating a stored impression—no one knows how recall works, but no one doubts that it exists—and, when activated, an impression from the past brings along not just simple raw information but visual images, emotional charges, and highly individual coloring. That's why no two family members have the same memories of how they were brought up. The screen of memory casts different movies for each one.

The fact that memories are individual is obvious, but why this is so remains mysterious. Somehow, we must account for the second human element, the self. The self is peculiar because it is made up of memories but also creates them. If you take all the labels that define your identity, such as race, gender, language, profession, etc., these are the accumulation of memory. If you lost those tags, would you be afflicted with severe amnesia or would you begin to identify with the witness (see page 155) that silently observes all mental activity? No one knows.

Memory outside the brain opens speculation on several fronts. A classic research project begun in 1961 at the University of Virginia under the late psychiatrist Ian Stevenson discovered hundreds of cases of young children who remember past lives and whose accounts have been authenticated—typically the memory is of a violent or traumatic death. (As of 2007, the latest update, the number of cases had risen to over 2,500, which implies that remembering a past life is a much more common phenomenon than conventional belief might indicate.) Being able to cross the boundary that separates life and death implies that there is a self that transcends a single lifetime and has no regard for the boundaries of time.

On the one hand, human memory gives us freedom from the limitations of clock and calendar. Our minds are able to travel freely through the multidimensional space-time continuum, including glimpses into the future. On the other hand, memory traps us in illusion and confusion. As we grow older and gain a longer time perspective, the lines between past, present, and future become increasingly blurred, and events that took place decades ago seem as if they happened just yesterday. More severely, it is now thought that mental disorders like anxiety and depression are at least partially learned behaviors that keep returning because we cannot un-remember them.

This sketch barely touches on the mystery of human memory, but it makes clear how unstable, fickle, transient, unreliable, and complicated the whole area of human memory is. This brings us back to the notion of writing memories in air; that is, escaping the problems caused by memory. If you could do that, the following would happen:

You would no longer be hurt by painful memories.

You would live in the present.

You would not be subject to the distortions and illusions of memory.

Your awareness would be a clean slate.

You wouldn't be fixated on the story you have been living since you were born.

You would experience lightness of being.

The reason these things aren't happening is due to the workings of memory. The burden of the past is entangled in everything you call "I, me, and mine." To drop this burden, you cannot expect your ego-personality to help, because it is entirely the creation of memory, and therefore it clings to the past with tenacious stubbornness. The only answer is to transcend memory, which is what "written in air" means. You align yourself not with your ego-personality, which is heavy and drags you down, but with something much simpler and more basic, something light: your sense of self.

Your sense of self is unaffected by time. It is the simple experience of "I am" that has always been with you. "I am" gets filled in by "I am X" or "I am Y," but this doesn't have to happen. Beyond I am hungry, I am smart, I am male, I am a musician, or any sentence beginning with "I am," there is "I am" itself. When you align yourself with the fact that you exist and are aware of existing, everything changes. Functional memory continues to work—your body and brain don't forget what they are supposed to be doing.

But personal memory loses its grip. This happens because "I am" is the gateway to pure consciousness, which is your true source. From this source flow intelligence, creativity, love, compassion, insight, and bliss. These are the highest values in life, and we deserve to access them without the interference of memory. None of these values has to be learned and remembered. They are innate; you were designed to experience them firsthand. That's the ultimate promise of "written in air," which is how our memories should be.

# Who's Minding the Store?

One of the strangest mysteries in everyday life is that it is much easier to stay alive than to be alive in the first place. There's a cascade of processes inside us that is perfectly synchronized—a body remains alive as long as its organs are alive, organs remain alive as long as tissues are alive, and tissues remain alive as long as cells are alive. This cascade has been understood for centuries, and yet no one knows why cells are alive to begin with. They don't deserve to be, because the teeming chemical reactions inside a heart, liver, or brain cell can easily be reproduced in a test tube without showing any signs of life.

As we've discussed earlier, science is far more comfortable asking "how" than "why," and if you investigate how cells operate, clear-cut conclusions can be drawn about the microscopic processes inside a cell that is analyzed using biochemistry tools. The bottom line is that 99 percent of biology centers on the "how" of living things. The nagging question of "Why?" is ignored as basically unscientific. Unfortunately, there is no "how" without "why." If two cars collide, the physics of one machine crashing into another is cut-and-dried, but to really explain what happens, you must determine if one driver was distracted by a phone call, was drunk, or something else.

The human quotient is crucial in everything we do, yet somehow it also applies to cells. Consider the necessities of being alive in a body. Cells must cooperate and communicate with one another; they have to live together in peace and place the well-being of the whole body ahead of their personal well-being. This is evident by the way cells are willing to die when their usefulness has reached an end— malignant cancer cells, on the other hand, multiply with a frenzy to avoid dying, and yet, in the end, they and the whole body perish.

Take all the human qualities that cells exhibit—the list also includes repelling invaders, telling friend from foe at the level of microorganisms, along with much, much more—and what you see is massively coordinated intelligence. Far from being inferior to human IQ, the intelligence of the body surpasses the capacity of modern medicine to explain it fully. So it is plausible to say that the mystery of life comes down to the emergence of intelligence where previously only raw chemistry ruled on primeval Earth.

This inrush of intelligence couldn't have come out of nowhere. The search for its roots cannot stop with chemistry. The most recent advanced explorations have gone to a subtler level of Nature—the quantum field—giving rise to quantum biology. If you want to know who is minding the store to keep life going, the quantum field might hold the answer.

Oddly, this deeper dive is both logical and absurd at the same time. It is logical because science operates by the reductionist method, reducing all phenomena to their smallest fundamental constituent. The absurdity comes in because a quantum can be billions of times smaller than an organic molecule, like the proteins that run the basic operations inside a cell. Going quantum takes us farther away from our day-to-day picture of life, not closer.

Yet appearances are deceiving. The secret of life isn't tiny; it's invisible, because intelligence is invisible. The promise of quantum biology is to witness behavior at the finest level of Nature that looks intelligent. If we examine how quantum biology applies the principles of quantum physics to living things, the cascade of life inside our bodies becomes consistent and continuous, revealing how holistic life really is.

One of the most striking parallels between the quantum and the macro world is known as "superposition," which defies the commonsense notion that nothing can be in two places at once. But from a quantum perspective there are states in which biomolecules are in superpositions, meaning that two or more states can coexist at the same time in the same place—the celebrated Schrödinger's cat is an example, a paradox in which the cat is dead and alive at the same time (not a real cat, since this is a thought experiment).

Likewise, two subatomic particles separated by any amount of space can somehow know what is happening to each other instantaneously, sending messages faster than the speed of light. Quantum biology might thus explain how brain cells in different locations seemingly coordinate without sending electrical or chemical signals to each other.

Other examples of quantum processes in biology include migratory bird navigation, which seems to involve detecting tiny changes in the Earth's magnetic field, and the way our senses work: Vision is possible because the retina can capture photons, which are quantum packets of light energy. It is beginning to make more and more sense to view the entire human brain as a quantum detector, in fact.

Yet quantum measurements are still not adequate to explain life. Inside a cell, life employs billions of relationships between thousands of protein types in comparison with about one hundred types of particles in quantum physics. And as it becomes obvious that science must explain how consciousness arose, explanations from physics have stumbled over the problem that a thought, feeling, or sensation isn't physical. Protests that everything must have a physical explanation, which is the basic worldview of mainstream science, run afoul of the fact that no one can point to a quantum, atom, or molecule that thinks.

This is why the picture must be reversed. It isn't true that matter created mind, but it might be true that mind created matter. With every thought you have, you generate new chemicals at the level of the synapses in your brain, and if you feel frightened, you might trigger a cascade of stress hormones that need your fear in order to be created. From the viewpoint of consciousness, there is creative intelligence at every level of Nature. Every system in Nature—from a quantum through atoms, molecules, cells, tissues, organs, and eventually the human body and brain— can mind itself.

That is, it is self-organizing, self-maintaining, in touch

with the systems above and below it in complexity, synched into the whole "system of systems" that is the human body (and the universe). Minding the store is the essence of living systems at every level. The advance of quantum biology has the advantage of showing that living behavior permeates creation. As noted earlier, what used to be called "the Great Chain of Being" that Christian theologians traced to the Godhead is now the great chain of consciousness. Without deifying it, we can embrace it as the best explanation for why life exists and not merely how.

# What If Everything Is Alive?

One of the great failures of science is still haunting us—the failure to discover why living things are alive. One of the most promising theories was known as "vitalism," which held that some undiscovered "life force" or "spark of life" separates living things like trees, cats, and amoebas from nonliving things like rocks, water, and salt. Vitalism was once so promising that the Nobel Prize was given to a champion of vitalism, the French philosopher Henri Bergson, in 1927. But, significantly, the prize was in literature, since no one, however enamored of vitalism, could provide scientific evidence for any kind of life force.

The tables were decisively turned to favor the opposite of vitalism, known as "functionalism," which breaks life down into physical processes like metabolism, growth, reproduction, adaptation, evolution, and extinction. That's where we find ourselves today, which poses a huge problem. Vitalism and functionalism are opposites, which implies that in the game of either/or, if one is false, the other must be true. But, unfortunately, functionalism doesn't explain life, either. It explains how life behaves, which isn't the same thing.

Why not? Because behavior comes down to chemistry and physics in the worldview of functionalism, but the physical "stuff" of creation obeys laws so rudimentary that they have very little bearing on living things: Imagine trying to explain the Eiffel Tower in terms of the behavior of the iron atoms that constitute it. It is true that the Eiffel Tower is made entirely of iron, but the same is true of a lump of iron ore buried in the Earth's crust. An iron atom must pass through a lot of stages before it turns into an edifice. It is fatal to functionalism that the vast majority of these stages involve the mind, and mind has no physical explanation.

For the moment let's accept that this last statement is true. Cries of protest will be raised against it from materialists, who will never abandon the notion that mind, or consciousness, must have a physical basis. That "must" is akin to the notion, if you are religious, that God must exist. In both cases, "must" precedes proof. The laws of Nature that govern physics and chemistry operate perfectly, but the creation of life doesn't follow from them. Life breaks the cardinal rule that two atoms or molecules coming together will always behave in the same ordained way. It's like a mother insisting that her children are perfect, even though they misbehave all the time.

Nature has done a fantastic job of misbehaving, particularly when it comes to the creation of mind, or consciousness. Nothing physical could have predicted it. Chemistry and physics view Nature as turbulent, random activity. A random number generator could never produce the beauty of Einstein's equation $E = mc^2$. Or if it could, the process would take as much time as the fabled monkeys who supposedly could write all of Shakespeare's plays by randomly hitting typewriter keys for millions of years. That's how the baffling contradiction arose between order and chaos in the universe. Obviously, they coexist, but no one can explain why one atom or molecule becomes part of a complex structure like the human brain while the exact same kind of atom or molecule drifts aimlessly in random fashion.

The bottom line is that vitalism and functionalism both seem to be wrong in different ways. Vitalism recognizes the meaning of life without a physical basis. Functionalism describes the behavior of living things without explaining why they occur.

At the present moment, with functionalism in the ascendant, salvaging it as a viable model has turned quantum. Unlike the rigid cause-and-effect of atoms and molecules, quanta are defined by such principles as uncertainty, action at a distance, the alternation between balance (quantum coherence) and imbalance (quantum de-coherence), and entanglement (the invisible ties between subatomic particles), all of which add new wrinkles and open new doors. The vast orderliness of the human body involves perfect self-organization at every level. While the physics of creation before the quantum revolution was about creating order out of chaos (which remains totally mysterious), quantum physics can point to order at the most basic level of Nature.

It seems like a major step forward to see creation as "order out of order," rather than "order out of chaos." But what about mind? In the end, it doesn't matter how perfectly tiny bits of matter behave if you can't show how they learned to think. This is the dead end that dooms functionalism, even though there are likely to be breakthroughs in new fields like quantum psychology, given that the human brain displays some basic quantum functions.

But rather than rescuing functionalism, there is another path. What struck the generation of quantum pioneers more than a century ago was how the behavior of quanta imitated life. Subatomic particles seem to move out of a state of uncertainty by deciding about what to do next. Viewing the whole apparatus of creation, some physicists began to wonder if the universe is much more like a great mind than a great machine. Take that insight a step further. Instead of quantum particles imitating life, what if they are actually alive?

One aspect of this conjecture is already becoming fashionable in the notion of "panpsychism," which holds that creation contains consciousness, or proto-consciousness, as a fundamental property like gravity. Panpsychism arose to rescue physics from the conundrum of not being able to explain consciousness. Instead of explaining it, panpsychism simply says that consciousness has always been there. Is this an insight or a clever ploy?

No one can really come to a consensus in response to that one. The problem echoes the old problem with vitalism—that you can't find a physical basis for the life force. What if you don't have to? The next step in explaining the origins of life involves giving up on the wrong avenues of exploration.

What we are ultimately talking about is a living human universe. It is too uncanny to posit that human DNA and the human brain appeared from random processes by an incredible throw of the dice. Even if there are billions of solar systems elsewhere in the cosmos that contain planets that might produce organic chemicals fit to evolve into living creatures, this does us no good if your explanation about life is fatally flawed. The origin of life in a human universe belongs to life itself. Take two attributes of human existence—creativity and intelligence—and there is no level of creation that doesn't reflect them.

If that's true, then instead of looking out at a dead creation that evolved to become alive, the universe becomes life itself, evolving through creativity and intelligence to produce every variety of living thing. Such a theory turns the telescope around, but why not? Looking through it, as modern science does now, has yielded tantalizingly close but no real answers.

# "You Are What You Eat"
# Should Be "You Are What You Ate"

There have been exciting discoveries about the microbiome that lead to a radical change in how we view the human body. *Microbiome* is a new name for something long known about—the teeming colonies of bacteria and fungi that exist all around the body. We need these microorganisms in order to digest food, but the existence of so-called "intestinal flora" isn't news, either. So why did the microbiome become so exciting?

The biggest reason can be summarized as "The microbiome is us." Instead of being invaders or microscopic hitchhikers, the microbiome represents the continuity of life itself. Microbial DNA is woven into human DNA, which immediately tells us that far from being enemy germs, thousands of species of bacteria, viruses, and fungi brought our ancestors the news of the world as it applies to the evolution of life. A cloud of DNA moves in, around, and through every living thing.

In natural-history museums, our hominid ancestors look small and primitive, but there is an invisible link that binds us to them—the microbiome. There are other microbiome locations in the mouth, on the skin, and in the armpits and groin, but let's limit ourselves to the gut microbiome, since it is incredibly complex, with an estimated two thousand species of microbial life, and it is life-giving.

Trying to grasp what is going on in the process of digestion is like trying to give a cloud sharp edges, because everyone's microbiome is constantly shifting. From day to day, the exact population is different. This also makes it very difficult to define the ideal microbiome. But what our ancestors ate defines what you eat today. "You are what you ate" tells the story of your life today, too, because the partnership, or symbiosis, between microbes and the rest of the body begins at birth.

From that moment onward, the gut microbiome was deeply involved in the following issues: the strength of your immune system, your allergies or lack of them, the status of inflammation in your body (inflammation, as noted earlier, is now suspected as the chief culprit, along with stress, in most if not all chronic disorders), your appetite and digestion, and even your emotions, since there's a direct pathway in the nervous system, called the gut-brain axis, between the brain, the digestive tract, and the main nerves that carry information about breathing, heart rate, and your perception of the outside world.

Right now, there are more clues perhaps than a solid understanding of the microbiome. The emerging popularity of prebiotics and probiotics, for example, seems like a good thing but it is based on wobbly science. Swallowing millions of microbes in a pill barely encroaches on the trillions that reside in your digestive tract. Certain findings are very tantalizing, however.

One major trend isn't going our way. In recent decades, dietary patterns in North America and elsewhere have undergone major changes, with increased amounts of red meat, high-fat foods, and refined sugars. This "Westernization" of diets, combined with a sedentary lifestyle, has resulted in modifications to the gut microbiome, which may partially contribute to a greater incidence of inflammatory disorders, such as heart disease, obesity, inflammatory bowel disorder, and even depression.

*Suggested action:* Promote what everyone's microbiome prefers, a whole-foods diet; a wide range of fiber (the food of the microbiome) from plants, grains, and nuts; and an anti-inflammatory diet in general.

Your intestines contain almost the entire ecosystem of bacteria in your body, and bacteria comprise the major population of the microbiome. While humans are genetically almost identical to one another as a species and around 85 percent identical to mice, bacteria are very divergent genetically among themselves. This implies that maximum diversity is key to a healthy microbiome.

*Suggested action:* Don't limit your diet to just a few favorite foods. Make your diet as diverse as possible.

While bacteria comprise about 2 to 4 pounds of our body weight, they vastly outnumber human cells. The microbiome contains some 3.3 million genes, compared with the 19,000 in the human genome. This genetic diversity leads to a vast array of protein products with a far greater spectrum of properties than those produced by the human body itself. Gut bacteria participate in the synthesis of vitamins, neurotransmitters, and essential amino acids, along with the transformation of bile acids and drug metabolism, to name but a few of their roles.

*Suggested action:* Become more open-minded and positive about microbes; avoid the trap of germophobia. There is enormous promise in bacteria as sources of new drugs, a decrease in chronic disorders, and longer, healthier life spans. At the very least, be humble in the face of these microbes, our most powerful evolutionary allies. The collective gene pool of life on Earth is almost entirely that of the microbiota.

The relative balance between different types of bacteria in our gut is a general bellwether for wellness. For example, obesity is correlated with reduced microbial diversity, specifically an increased ratio of Firmicutes (one broad group of bacteria) to Bacteroidetes (another broad group of bacteria). A mere 20 percent shift in bacterial abundance from Bacteroidetes to Firmicutes causes an extra 150 calories gained per day, translating into three pounds of weight gain every two months. Firmicutes are proinflammatory and promote obesity, while Bacteroidetes provide a counterbalance.

***Suggested action:*** Focus on the microbiome as the source of, and remedy for, obesity. This implies once again that an organic whole-foods diet is key to wellness. Obesity is just one aspect of this approach; there are implications for everything from immunity to psychological symptoms.

The brain and the microbiome engage in two-way communication, and the signals being sent from one to the other deal with everything that is happening chemically in your body, as well as neurologically. In the most fundamental way, every cell eavesdrops on every other cell, and what harms one system harms the whole. The focus here is on the stress response and the immune response. A healthy microbiome, by implication, communicates to the rest of the body, setting up feedback loops that promote well-being.

*Suggested action:* The more we know about the microbiome, the more critical the need for stress reduction. This is the message that should cut through all the noise about medical advice, drugs, and diet. Get a good night's sleep, take active measures to reduce the daily stress you experience, particularly the repeated small stresses we tend to overlook, and go back to Nature in what you eat.

The suggested actions we've offered are neither new nor radical. Most sound like proper advice heard over and over again. But the microbiome reinforces two overriding facts. The mind and the body are a whole, a bodymind, and this bodymind is dominated, genetically speaking, by the bacteria that inhabit us. From these two facts alone an entirely new and better view of human well-being is already developing.

# Order Out of Chaos:
# Why You Aren't a Hurricane

One of the mysteries of human existence is the fact that you do not fly apart into a cloud of atoms and molecules but instead hold together as a living, breathing, thinking organism. It is said that we live on the edge of chaos, because the human body has adapted to counter an enormous range of accidents, mistakes, wounds, illnesses, and stresses that would destroy a nonliving system.

A simple example is your joints. You bend and unbend your fingers hundreds of times a day. Take a bar of steel and bend it hundreds of times. It will break, which your fingers don't. In fact, they get better at whatever they are doing, such as practicing the piano, a repeated activity that creates more order, even though playing the piano or the violin demands unending movements that look random if you happen to be deaf.

The study of chaos has progressed far enough that you can take any phenomenon, from the weather to a beating heart, traffic patterns to brain waves, and view it as the contest between order and chaos. Your life depends on the predictable (orderly) sequence of events that produces a healthy heartbeat, and if the sequence gets out of sync, the heart can go into irregular activity anywhere from a benign irregular heartbeat (arrhythmia) to a random convulsion (fibrillation) that proves fatal.

This makes it seem that order is preferable to chaos. Most people would agree that an orderly life without too much unpredictability in it is better than a chaotic life filled with random accidents and unforeseen events. But, in reality, order isn't better than chaos. They are two sides of a balancing act. Taking the human body as an example, order and chaos are balanced in countless ways. Here are some of the most important.

- Biochemicals rush randomly throughout your bloodstream, but once they enter a cell, they contribute to the orderly processes that build and maintain every cell.
- When the heart becomes irregular, problems might arise, yet a rigid drumlike heartbeat is also unhealthy and can indicate chronic stress.

To be healthy, your heartbeat needs to respond flexibly to whatever you are doing and whatever is happening to you. This is called heart rate variability and it correlates with good health.

• The brain preserves orderly operations in every part of the body, but the activity of brain cells is highly chaotic, while during a seizure, such as an epileptic attack, the pattern of brain activity is abnormally orderly.

In chaos theory there are two basic principles that deepen the mystery of life while attempting to explain it. The first is popularly known as the Butterfly Effect, which we touched upon in part three. It says that a butterfly moving its wings in one part of the globe can create a tiny air turbulence that expands on its own until a hurricane is created in another part of the globe. Your body must keep these tiny disruptions in check or a swirling vortex in your bloodstream might create a cataclysm. But you are safe from turning into a hurricane. Your body has all kinds of balancing mechanisms to keep hundreds if not thousands of processes within their normal range.

The second principle is commonly called "the edge of chaos," which holds that orderly systems depend on being able to survive chaos when it strikes, while at the same time not being too rigid, routine, and predictable. This is akin to the Buddhist adage that a mighty oak topples in a storm while a limber sapling bends in the wind and survives.

Chaos theory has much more to say about vital issues like heartbeat, respiration, brain activity, the immune system, and the like, but let's stick with the Butterfly Effect and the edge of chaos. Nature got along very well for billions of years letting chaos reign in its domain and order presiding over its domain. Swirling chaos characterized the Big Bang, yet in time atoms and molecules formed stable systems. Letting chaos reign didn't prevent order from having its days, which resulted in stars, planets, Earth, and life on Earth. This is the progression to higher states of order we call evolution.

Yet evolution cannot actually defeat the dissipation of heat energy that is inevitable, known as entropy. Nature wants heat to be evenly dispersed everywhere, so hot spots give off their heat until they cool down to the same temperature that surrounds them. Why, then, did evolution and entropy come to a cooperative agreement? Since birth, your body grew and developed, which is evolution in action, and yet living forms must die and decay, too, which is pure entropy.

Now we find ourselves at the heart of the matter. There is no third force to mediate or referee the opposition of evolution and entropy, no physical force, at least. If you look at the bigger picture, however, it seems that both concepts—order and chaos—are mind-made fictions. To see this, imagine Leonardo da Vinci painting the *Mona Lisa*. The portrait is a beautiful example of order, but if you took a close-up of Leonardo's palette, you would see his brush randomly dabbing at various colors without any seeming order.

Yet somehow the disorder of a dabbing brush and the order of the *Mona Lisa* serve one purpose that transcends both of them. The portrait isn't simplistic order, like lining up pennies in a row. It represents an invisible intention that has nothing to do with the processes that lead to its fulfillment. The intention to create art goes beyond such activities as gathering bristles into paintbrushes, mining cobalt to turn it into a blue pigment, and chopping down trees in order to make the frames on which canvas is stretched before the first dab of paint is applied.

In every human affair, the same invisible third force arranges how chaos is kept from destroying order and how order is kept from getting so rigid that life stops. This third force isn't physical, because science, which has a complex if not thorough knowledge of the physical world, can't explain why entropy and evolution came to such perfect agreement in Nature.

In all humility we cannot say (although it has been said thousands of times) that creativity and intelligence only arose with *Homo sapiens* or at best our hominid ancestors. In this book we have presented the case for Nature itself embodying creative intelligence. This line of thinking still eludes science, but, in the end, it might be the only logical explanation that works. Otherwise, we would all be hurricanes or rocks, the two alternatives of chaos out of control and orderliness stuck in place for eons.

# Your Brain's Most Important Relationship Is Not with You

You can't have a thought, feeling, sensation, or mental image without calling on your brain, and this close relationship makes us human. Since 100 billion brain cells are constantly generating your mental life, no relationship seems more important, and everyone has a fear in the back of their mind about what might happen in old age if Alzheimer's strikes, in essence destroying the mind-brain connection.

But as precious as this relationship is, your brain has a more important relationship that was hidden until about twenty years ago. This precious relationship is with bacteria, and even when you are asleep or thinking about nothing at all, the communication never ceases between the brain and bacteria, specifically the bacteria in your gastrointestinal tract (the gut microbiota).

Between them, the brain and your GI tract have created a real-life matrix, just like the one in science fiction. You are alive and relate to your brain inside this tight structure of biochemicals that carry thousands of messages per second between your microbiota and your brain. At first sight this seems unbelievable, because few life-forms have genetics as rudimentary as a bacterium, and no lifeform has a brain as complex as the human brain. An old proverb says that even a cat can look at a king. Biologically speaking, the lowly bacterium (along with viruses and microscopic fungi) does a lot more than look at your brain, more even than eavesdropping on it.

The trillions of bacteria in the microbiota feed off the indigestible parts of the food you consume (i.e., fiber and so-called resistant starches), a fact taught in every health class in school. Digestion supplies the energy and nutrients that keep us alive, so it looks like a basic and therefore crude process. But digestion is an evolutionary miracle. Bacteria thrived for billions of years doing whatever they wanted to do, and at an invisible level they rule the planet, along with fungi and viruses. They are the master DNA of life on Earth.

Since some of these microorganisms cause disease and decay, it's easy to see them as a threat, and most people still do. If you consider life to be survival of the fittest, bacteria are much more fit than we are, and it is amazing that at least one or two thousand species of bacteria decided to support human life. Taking up residence on the skin, on the surface of moist mucous tissue like the lining of the mouth and nose, and, far more important, in the GI tract, bacteria wove themselves into our own DNA.

They make a healthy immune system possible. They help synchronize the body's many clocks (biorhythms), beginning with sleep. They modulate our response to stress, inflammation, and probably our susceptibility to all manner of chronic disorders, including cancer. Should the flourishing bacterial colonies in your GI tract get disturbed, you may experience a cascading effect of enormous consequences. The fact that microscopic bacteria can lead to wholesale disruptions in the body may seem like throwing a baseball through the window of a skyscraper and having the entire building collapse.

The chemical story of how this occurs is so complex that a complete understanding is far away, if it will ever be achieved. But some lessons have emerged, such as the following:

- The body is not so much a physical object as a matrix of intelligence in which information is constantly updated.

- The first part of your body to be alerted to any event—mental or physical—is the microbiota.
- The most serious impairment of the microbiota and the whole matrix stems from stress, chronic inflammation, and poor-quality sleep. Also among the top sources of disturbances are anxiety and depression.
- Placing an emphasis on good-quality sleep and lower stress is just as important as what you eat, even though the quality of your diet obviously affects your microbiota.
- Your microbiota is continually shifting in very complex ways that cannot be monitored constantly. This places the burden of wellness on your lifestyle choices.

Because people are fixated on diet and diet is critical for a healthy microbiota, some guidelines about what to eat are necessary. One basic fact must never be forgotten or neglected: These microorganisms feed on the indigestible parts of the food you eat; in other words, the fiber in plant-based foods. The more varied your sources of vegetable fiber, the better, which is largely why the Mediterranean diet is so salubrious.

Humans do not have the genetic potential to produce

the enzymes that break down this fibrous material. A few other findings are relevant. Interestingly, eating cooked white rice or baked potatoes after they cool down increases their resistant starch quality and feeds the symbiotic microbes in the gut better. Ironically, potato chips, which are heated, then cooled, in a sense have become a new "health food." The same idea applies to freezing bananas or eating green bananas. Soaking raw oats in milk or yogurt overnight is another good idea that provides resistant starch.

Lentils, whole grains, cashews, and flaxseed are examples of foods with high resistant-starch content. All vegetables, fresh berries, and fruits provide a rich source of soluble fiber, indigestible carbohydrates, minerals, and vitamins, which the average person does not consume enough of. Switching from the typical American diet to an organic, whole-foods diet with a strong foundation in plant-based food is a tall order, but at least the science is there.

Where science isn't there, one can affirm, is explaining the matrix that is the web of life. All evolutionary time is contained inside us. Life is supported by constant intelligent communication, and although the chemical carriers are fairly well known, with more discoveries on the way, the most fundamental mystery remains unsolved. What reason is there for bacteria to learn to talk to the brain or to benefit human life in the first place? We only know that this has occurred. No one could have made the story up, and in the end the human brain may be incapable of grasping how the matrix works, because that would be like explaining every drop in Niagara Falls while the water is moving.

What we know so far about keeping the matrix healthy is barely a beginning. The flow of creative intelligence cannot be observed directly, and the link between mind and matter is almost as murky today as it was for the ancient Greeks. Everyone has a pet theory about these interconnected enigmas. Meanwhile, without thanks and often without being noticed, the mystery has been content to re-create life every second for three billion years.

# The Wisdom of the
# Body Is the Wisdom of Now

Time is as mysterious as life itself. As a statement of fact, this is undeniable. Everything about a living cell is timed. Cells know when to divide, which requires DNA to split down the middle like a genetic zipper. Each half rebuilds the entire double helix through precise molecular timing, one half working from front to back, the other half from back to front. So-called molecular machines oversee this process, which isn't continuous but sometimes requires a pause. Once the two halves are whole again, the rest of the cell must parcel itself out so that a perfect replica of every part, including the outside membrane, seamlessly emerges.

What we're talking about is a complete mastery of time—and there are thousands of other processes involved, because your body doesn't run on a single clock (or bio-rhythm). It synchronizes a bewildering number of clocks, each with its own duration. Quantum biology has come closer to unraveling how time affects aging and disease than any previous theory. The basic points you have already encountered.

- Entropy degrades the use of energy inside a cell. As time passes, quantum-scale errors cause energy to be used less efficiently.
- The tiniest local errors in a cell have consequences that spread to other cells, then to tissues, organs, and the whole body.
- The degradation of energy gives a quantum explanation for why we age and get sick.
- Time therefore is the culprit that invisibly robs us of life, and its behavior cannot be understood without going to the quantum level.

These points are accurate but frustrating at the same time. Going to the quantum level is a mathematical journey. Using advanced computation and artificial intelligence, an overwhelming amount of data can be extracted about quantum biology. Somewhere in this data are clues to the astonishing mastery of time that comes effortlessly to every cell in your body. But there is also a conceptual wall that must be scaled. No one knows where time comes from. On this side of the Big Bang, time, space, matter, and energy organize the cosmos. On the other side of the Big Bang lies unknown territory, and unfortunately, no data can be extracted from it.

Not just the origin of time is baffling. Examine the body's biological clocks, and you'll find all kinds of things just as baffling. To take just one, how does the body synchronize long-range time (including the loss of baby teeth for the emergence of mature teeth, the onset of puberty, and the arrival of menstruation), mid-range time (including the cycles of digestion, hormones, and sleep), and short-range time (including thousands of nearly instantaneous chemical processes at the cellular level)?

If you focus on this single mystery, a quantum clue emerges. Behind the body's ability to synchronize time, the timeless must be at work. That's because whatever organizes all these biological clocks isn't on a timer. So, who or what times it?

Imagine yourself sitting on the bank of a river. You can only know the speed of the water's current by not floating downstream with it. Just as there must be a vantage point outside the river, the quantum field gives a vantage point outside time.

This vantage point has a surprising name: *now*. Now is outside time. All the regulation, control, computation, and intelligence implied by synchronizing time cycles that are long-range, mid-range, and short-range occur in the now. This fact holds the key to what is popularly called the wisdom of the body. Your body assembles everything it needs effortlessly, and it does this here and now. One might truthfully say that the wisdom of the body is the wisdom of now. Medicine will be revolutionized if time can be understood in the now, because the now never ages. It isn't subject to entropy or the degradations traceable to time as the culprit of life.

Your body is comfortable living in the now. Yet now seems quite elusive psychologically. Wanting to live in the present moment is something many people find frustrating. They are told that life renews itself in the present moment, that the burden of the past masks the joy that is always available in the present. The problem is that these lovely promises are hard to translate into personal experience. You need to probe a little deeper to see what is really needed. There is wisdom in the now that isn't revealed to the mind without self-awareness.

It is the teeming, active mind that finds the present moment so elusive. Constantly occupied with thoughts, feelings, and sensations, the mind gives the impression that it is already present. This is an illusion. Consider the light coming at us from distant galaxies. Gazing at the night sky, this light seems to be shining here and now, but in fact it took billions of years for starlight to reach Earth, so the light you see is actually billions of years old.

Surprisingly, the same is true of what you see right this minute. In the very brief time it takes for the signals generated by photons of light to travel from your retina to the visual cortex in your brain, there is a delay. In effect, you are seeing the past, just as when you gaze at the stars. The same is true of the other senses as well. The rise and fall of perception brings a time delay. Likewise, the coming and going of thought is just an *impression* of being present. The vast majority of thoughts require an interpretation, which puts thinking even more in the past. Consider how a thought like "I am really hungry" can linger for hours until you get a chance to eat.

Yet you are always present in your mind even when this escapes your notice. This place where you are always present is in the silent gap between thoughts. A thought is transient, rising and fading away like a wave on the ocean.

Yet the ocean is always present, and so is the silent background of awareness that you glimpse, for a fraction of a second, between thoughts.

If you dive into this silent gap, which is the purpose of meditation, the awareness you experience is in the present moment. Silence has no bad memories, wounds, traumas, or conditioning from the past. Therefore, it can be present. Silence is continuous and new at the same time. The newness comes from the creative possibilities that human awareness contains. Not all of these possibilities are new. When your mind delivers its next thought, in all likelihood it will repeat or resemble a past thought. Habits of thinking are the main reason we do not experience the present moment.

Your body has no such problem. Cells are always present—they have to be, in order to survive. Your cells do not store a supply of oxygen and nutrients for more than a few seconds. They depend on being nourished without worrying about the future. In other words, they trust in the wisdom of now. If a cell could voice what this wisdom consists of, it would say that the now

Is always new

Knows what is needed at all times

Refreshes the experience of being alive

Contains vibrant energy

Has no regrets about the past or apprehension about
the future

These are the very qualities the mind seeks in the present moment. Yet there is actually nothing to seek, because
the now occupies no space in time. It cannot be seized or
described. There is no "there there" by the standards of the
thinking mind, which craves to hold on to pleasurable experiences and banish painful ones. The now isn't about
pleasure or pain.

Once you realize this, you have taken the most important step to being in the present moment: Stop believing
that you can get there by thinking, feeling, believing, hop-
ing, or any other mental process. The wisdom of now, as
your body already knows in its trillions of cells, is embedded in existence itself. Without this wisdom, a cell cannot
exist. The illusion that you can exist without the wisdom of
now must be discarded.

The wisdom of now cannot be explained rationally,
using measurements, data, or mathematical formulas, but
science can use these tools to spot some fascinating clues.

If you take a beaker and fill the bottom with ink and the top with clear water, over time the two will mix. The random motion of molecules in the ink and water is governed by entropy and the arrow of time. Time's arrow moves only in one direction, so ink and water will mix going forward in time. They are fantastically unlikely to separate into two liquids, ink and water, in their individual compartments.

This intimate link between entropy and time is a bedrock of classical physics. But instead of a beaker, look at a cell. It is basically a container filled with molecules of all sorts, not just two, like ink and water, but tens of thousands of different kinds of molecules. According to entropy, operating through the random motion of molecules, a cell should be an even mixture where every molecule is randomly distributed throughout.

Yet a cell, far from being a mixture ruled by entropy, divides itself into compartments with hundreds of separate processes, and each process precisely uses the molecules it needs, far more precisely than Rembrandt mixing the colors on his palette to get exactly the tints and hues he wants. Quantum biology allows data to be extracted that measure just how precisely a cell uses its energy resources. What cannot be measured, however, is the invisible intelligence that does everything in time, not too early or too late. Now rules the life of a cell. Only now stands still and directs where energy and molecules need to go, like a traffic cop standing on an island directing the whizzing cars all around him.

The physics that governs how ink and water mix is defined inside a cell, yet it can't be said that the actual proteins, enzymes, water, and genes in a cell "know" anything. Not in their physical makeup, at least. There are no physical properties that create intelligence, much less wisdom, of the kind that a cell exhibits. What this says is that entropy and the arrow of time are linked, but entropy doesn't *explain* time. Without consciousness, there is ultimately no necessity to enter time into many quantum equations, where the position of a subatomic particle in space can be interchanged with its position in time and its energy state.

All experience occurs in consciousness. Without awareness, the world "out there" has no sights, sounds, textures, smells, and tastes. That part can't be questioned, because at face value we all know that in deep sleep there is no world "out there," not for us as experiencers. Here the wisdom of now takes a strange twist. In deep sleep, according to the Vedic seers, you experience pure awareness, which makes sleep the closest anyone comes to the total absence of illusion.

We know that this reasoning sounds strange, and the

automatic response is that sleep contains no experience at all if you aren't dreaming. But this is because the haze of the conditioned mind overlaps from your waking hours into your sleep. With clarity of awareness, you would perceive sleep as the quiet peace of pure awareness. In fact, you have to go there in order for your brain to clear the slate and rid itself of accumulated toxins, two things it cannot do while you are awake and thinking.

Few people are likely to perceive total clarity when they are asleep, but the wisdom of now is glimpsed in waking hours, too. These glimpses come when you experience anything the mind cannot create and never has. By now you are well aware of what those things are: love, compassion, insight, empathy, truth, beauty, inspiration, joy, wonder, creativity, and inner growth. No one invented them. They cannot be invented but are innately part of human awareness. They are our interpretation of pure awareness made manifest.

The ultimate reason you don't need to seek the present moment is that it is already finding you instead, in those moments when the silent gap between thoughts delivers these gifts. If the silent gap were empty, spiritual life would be just as empty and pure awareness a void. But in reality, infinite possibilities exist in pure awareness, and the gap between thoughts is the portal for activating these possibilities. To be conscious of this reality takes you out of all illusions. Now you have a lifelong motivation for valuing the gifts of the now and doing everything you can to live by them.

# Summation

## The Big Takeaways

This part of the book has presented quantum answers to old scientific riddles. You have been given a road map to the new science of life. Yet our aim has been to create a shift in your awareness. We want you to absorb as fully as possible your connection to your quantum body. Quantum reality has a reputation for strangeness, as if Nature perversely created a menagerie of weirdly behaving particles that flout the physics and chemistry that operate in normal, everyday life.

Yet quantum reality, as we've tried to demonstrate, is the "real" reality, the foundation from which everything about you originates. The weird behavior exhibited at the quantum level conforms perfectly to how consciousness works. There is a profound connection between the breakthroughs made by the great quantum pioneers over a century ago and the most ancient and complete model of consciousness, which emerged from the Vedic seers of India thousands of years ago.

No matter how profound an answer might be, everyone is left to live the mystery of life. The simplest experiences— seeing the blue of the sky, tasting a grain of salt, hearing music—have no scientific explanation. That hasn't stopped researchers from constantly seeking one. The Vedic seers took a different path. They affirmed that consciousness is simple. It is the given, the point zero and ground state of existence. In 1931 Max Planck gave an interview to the *London Observer* that contained a passage we cited earlier: The interviewer asked, "Do you think that consciousness can be explained in terms of matter and its laws?"

"No," Planck replied, "I regard consciousness as fundamental. I regard matter as derivative from consciousness. We cannot get behind consciousness. Everything that we think about, everything that we regard as existing, postulates consciousness."

To get behind consciousness means solving where it comes from, how it was created, when and where this creation occurred, and other issues that apply to scientific discoveries. When Planck insisted that matter derived from consciousness, he made a Vedic statement. At the same time, he pointed the way for future investigation in quantum physics. It has taken nearly a century for Planck's lead to be followed. Now, with the advent of quantum metabolism and quantum biology, the link between quantum reality and the human body is open to discovery.

Such research occurs in abstract areas that do not seem to touch everyday life, but this book has revealed some critical issues in everyday life that need quantum answers and are now getting them.

*Entropy:* Entropy, as we've discussed, is a measure of disorder. For instance, as heat energy dissipates when an ice cube melts, a physical system displays increased entropy. All physical systems in the universe are subject to increased entropy—like ice cubes, stars dissipate their energy—with the goal of evenly dispersed energy everywhere in the cosmos. This is called the state of maximum entropy. A few of these issues are beginning to move to center stage and are likely to remain there for decades.

By contrast, a living biological system like the human body attempts to create organized complexity by lowering entropy, using the constant energy boost that comes from metabolizing food. Each of us is an island of negative entropy, as it is known, because our bodies organize energy more than we dissipate it.

Heat, a by-product of metabolic energy, has both positive and negative consequences. Heat is needed to maintain body temperature while its excess in the form of inflammation causes structural damage. This points to the important discovery that low-grade chronic inflammation is connected to the development of the chronic diseases associated with aging.

*Information:* Any physical object can be viewed not as a thing but as a storehouse of information—human DNA is an intricate example of huge information storage. So are the cells in your body, and this information is dynamic, being exchanged and moving around all the time, much as a computer operates. Cells thrive on high-information nutrition supplied by whole foods, while low-information foods (white sugar, white flour, and processed foods) are "empty" calories as far as what cells need. Therefore, instead of contributing to metabolism in a fruitful way, these low-information foods tend to be shunted away into fat cells, making them a leading contributor to obesity.

*Stress:* Although stress research goes back decades, its importance has been reaching deeper and deeper in recent years. The symptoms of stress used to be the main focus of attention. The biological stress response was designed to react to a brief, sharp emergency, after which the body returns to its normal state of functioning. But modern life has distorted the natural application of stress. The presence of low-level chronic stress doesn't give rise to brief, acute signs. It persists like a low-grade fever, and although life might continue to seem normal, at the cellular level, particularly in terms of hormones and the indicators of inflammation, chronic stress creates microscopic distortions that have macroscopic implications.

The quantum effects of stress are metabolic, meaning that the physics of energy distribution inside a cell is key. This is the same level, however, where a person's psychological response to stress has deteriorating effects, and where aging is connected to diminished efficiency in a cell's intertwined processes. A full picture of stress must embrace how we metabolize experiences, not just energy.

*Time:* We all know that aging is a function of time, but, to a physicist, "time's arrow" is created by entropy. Energy that dissipates is moving in one direction. An example is a glass that breaks after falling on the floor. It cannot be unbroken, and therefore the accident moved the arrow of time. In the case of the human body, the loss of efficiency in all kinds of processes also moves the arrow of time. Loss of biological efficiency can be measured as the process of aging. What matters most is how you biologically age, not how you look in the mirror.

These issues illustrate how the mystery of the human body is starting to be understood in a fresh light, aided by quantum theory. The measurements required are no different from measuring any other physical object, even though a structure like the human brain or human DNA is so complex that its "thingness" is almost unrecognizable as it relates to a melting ice cube, a decaying oak leaf, or the cooling down of the cosmos.

If you are a scientist trying to understand the human body, whatever is not measurable is left out of the picture. Yet all of us are in intimate contact with the mystery of life, and we can choose to live the mystery instead of waiting for experts to solve it with yet more research. The most basic way to live the mystery is to make a conscious connection with your quantum body. The connecting link is awareness. Everyone is equipped for this. When you feel tired or energetic, alert or dull, when you detect a headache coming on or go through the complex sensations of being pregnant, you are engaging in a process known as interoception.

We covered interoception in part one, but we need to underscore its importance. Interoception is the key to living the mystery. It is a genuine sixth sense, and in fact the five senses depend on it. That is because sight, sound, touch, taste, and smell need to be consciously interpreted. Unlike the five senses, which primarily pay attention to the outside world, interoception applies awareness to the body, and beyond that to the entire bodymind. Every cell eavesdrops on your thoughts, feelings, and sensations, so it is totally artificial to separate mind and body.

Besides uniting the two, interoception infuses the body with awareness. The wisdom of the body does not need your attention most of the time. Thousands of processes operate in perfect synchronization by using the creative intelligence in every cell. However, if you apply awareness in a conscious way, you enhance the body's wisdom. Conscious relaxation, meditation, performing yoga postures, reducing stress, eating a whole-foods diet, exercising, and getting regular good-quality sleep are all conscious interventions that spring from interoception. Something that cannot be reduced to physical data—your awareness—allows you to live the mystery that is not just your body but you as a human being.

The flow of creative intelligence that sustains life is also responsible for going beyond basic processes to deliver the experiences of higher or expanded awareness; namely love, compassion, beauty, truth, insight, creativity, bliss, and personal growth. These experiences require interoception in the form of sensitivity to what is happening "in here." Outside stimuli, like seeing someone you love or contemplating a work of art, do not create such experiences; at best, they trigger them. One person's rapture over music and art, for example, can leave another person indifferent or turned off.

We are not discounting the enormous benefits of medical science in understanding the human body. These benefits do not have to be discarded or ignored. Getting the latest COVID vaccine booster is only one example. But living the mystery is the only way to achieve lifelong fulfillment and personal evolution.

Now you know the big takeaways from this book. The reality of the quantum body has taken the combined knowledge of modern science and ancient wisdom. That's not a cliché or wishful thinking. The future of everyone's well-being—and the planet's—depends, in the final analysis, on bringing every creative impulse to bear, and our greatest hope lies at the source of all creative solutions, in consciousness itself.

# Epilogue

# The Spiritual Dimension

*by Deepak Chopra*

*The eye with which I see God*
*is the same with which God sees me.*
—MEISTER ECKHART

This book would be incomplete without discussing the spiritual dimension of life. Modern physics went in almost the opposite direction envisioned by the quantum pioneers. Many of them believed that the quantum world bordered on the soul or God or the transcendent. Heisenberg hit upon a memorable image. "The first gulp from the glass of natural sciences will turn you into an atheist, but at the bottom of the glass God is waiting for you."

Mostly the quantum pioneers avoided using religious terms, however. Their primary concern, when it came to the spiritual dimension, was consciousness, which has been my primary concern, too. I agree with Freeman Dyson's simple but profound insight, "I do not make any clear distinction between mind and God." A cosmic deity and a cosmic mind are one and the same.

I've encountered more people than ever before who have set out on their own spiritual path. They have become inspired by a vision of higher consciousness; they've gotten excited about "follow your bliss." The traditional search for God attracts fewer and fewer people. A term that was laughed at when I wrote *Quantum Healing*, "the evolution of consciousness," has become the focus for countless people on their personal journey.

A cynic might point out that we have been hearing about the emergence of higher consciousness for at least fifty years, and yet collective enlightenment isn't in sight. The reason is that with the evolution of consciousness, a straight-line path isn't feasible. Nothing in the quantum domain follows a straight line, so why should spirit?

Reaching higher consciousness follows a different path from any other goal you set for yourself. In every age and spiritual tradition, the path to higher consciousness is marked by some highly peculiar, even unique qualities:

You can't see the goal in advance.

You therefore cannot make reliable plans on how to achieve the goal.

Because your inner life is constantly shifting, you never know for certain if your approach is correct or even if you are equipped for the next phase of the journey.

Your ego-personality, which supports you in every other worthwhile activity (when it isn't sabotaging you or filling you with self-doubt), is of little use here. In fact, the ego-personality is an obstacle to higher consciousness or pulls away from any drastic change, particularly if old habits, beliefs, and conditioning are challenged.

All these points can be discussed at length, but I don't think I've misrepresented them. Once you absorb that your path must come to terms with everything on this list, the picture changes. You realize that you are like a surgeon performing surgery on himself, an impossible task. How can an individual guided by the ego-personality, with no set goal or reliable map in hand, ever evolve?

The answer is that a silent controller knows where you are going. It alone governs the path to higher consciousness. From your everyday viewpoint, the process is like watching the pieces of a jigsaw puzzle assemble themselves into a picture by moving themselves. The whole thing often feels uncanny. You must surrender yourself to a process that is dynamic, shifting, responsive to every life situation, and impossible to predict in advance.

To deepen the mystery, you don't even know *who* is on the path. The spiritual dimension is above and beyond the level of the ego. Even though you are used to thinking and acting as an individual "I," higher consciousness isn't personal: It is universal, holistic, and in the end inconceivable. This sounds intimidating, to indulge in understatement, but the same guidance that uses quantum principles to achieve well-being applies here. We let our true boundless nature come to light; we meet our true self, exchanging a series of provisional selves along the way for something closer to reality.

Your provisional selves, from birth to death and in

between, feel like "me." We own these personas; we assume we *are* them. But from a quantum perspective, every persona—newborn, infant, toddler, young child, adolescent, adult, and senior—is just a garment to clothe the ego, a superficial covering that masks the true self. The true self is the only part of us that knows reality, and it invisibly manages our evolution. Just as DNA unfolds a child's development on schedule, with a definite timeline that puts baby teeth, for example, ahead of puberty, the evolution of consciousness unfolds according to a timeline. But in spiritual matters the timeline is unpredictable. Nothing is known in advance. There is no "in advance." Evolution happens in the now, which is beyond our control, since "now" vanishes the instant we recognize it. It is hard to let go and surrender to a process you have no control over.

Children in India are told a lovely fable that goes to the heart of the matter:

A grand coach is being driven down the road pulled by six magnificent horses. The driver is urging the horses on when a soft voice from inside the coach says, "Stop." The driver has never heard this voice before, so he ignores it and urges the horses to go faster. Again, the soft voice from inside the coach says, "Stop."

Now the driver is irritated. Who does this impudent passenger think he is that he has a right to tell the driver what to do? The driver whips the horses into a frenzy, but the voice from inside the coach continues to say, "Stop." Only when the driver is totally exhausted does he cry, "Tell me who you are, for heaven's sake!"

From inside the invisible passenger says, "I am the owner of this coach." And with that, the driver stops.

This fable symbolizes the ego (driver) who thinks he is in control because he whips on the mind and the five senses (the six horses), not realizing that everything is in service of the true self (the invisible owner inside the coach). Only when you realize this reality will your active mind stop its frantic activity. Otherwise, the ego will whip everything faster and faster, driving you to the wrong destination.

Fables don't have the power to change our lives, but they can point us in the right direction. Having heard the soft voice of the true self/soul/Atman, what should you do then? Relax and trust. Everything is controlled by cosmic mind, with each of us acting as its conduit. (I think of another saying from Freeman Dyson: "We are the chief inlets of God on this planet.") Yet whether or not you decide to surrender is an empty choice made according to what your ego-personality feels at the moment. In reality, an inconceivable project is unfolding, one that is dismantling the whole setup of your existence to arrive at the true self, God, the soul, Atman, Buddhist *satori*, unity consciousness, or enlightenment—whatever you want to call it.

The setup of everyone's life is a dramatic confrontation of opposites. The conventional tags we apply to this clash of opposites—pleasure versus pain, good versus evil, light versus darkness, love versus fear, God versus the Devil— are mind-made. Viewed cosmically, there is either evolution or entropy. Entropy is on the side of decay and destruction, but evolution takes the opportunity after each act of destruction to invent a new creation.

On the personal level, evolution proceeds when we dismantle some self-destructive aspect of the ego-personality so that a more evolved quality can take its place. A loving gesture defeats fear. Compassion defeats selfishness. Beauty defeats ugliness. Truth defeats lies. If you focus on your own evolution, the path to higher consciousness remains inconceivable, but you will be aligned with the cosmic design. Someone else flies the plane, but you get to your destination as a passenger even though you have no control of the cockpit.

It is helpful to trust that the true self knows better than you which parts of the setup must come to the surface and when. Trust brings peace of mind. Destruction is inevitable, a fact that troubles spiritual life and always has. "Why did God do this to me?" and "What kind of God allows this to happen?" are age-old questions. They are never answered because no one can read God's mind. Nor can you read cosmic mind. But you can know how it reaches you here on the ground, through the workings of creative intelligence.

The darkness, being essential in the cycle of creation and destruction, is not to be feared or denied. As Rumi beautifully put it, "You have a death and return in every moment—every moment the world is renewed." Our strategy as evolving selves is to patiently confront every sign of darkness, accepting that the light will find a way to overcome it. There is no need to use the tools of darkness against it, either, since violence, resistance, despair, hatred, and fear are not how the light operates. The light is nothing but awareness revealing something new about itself, bringing the true self, which is universal, into the equation.

To the extent that we are able, each of us must remember that the true self is the real self. Only by standing firm in who we really are can the evolution of consciousness take hold every day throughout our lifetime. In a never-ending journey, now is the portal to eternity, and the best way to use your time is to invite the timeless to guide you.

# Acknowledgments

## Deepak Chopra

For me, the secret of keeping my thoughts fresh is to continually learn from many sages and scientists over the decades. I'm grateful to my coauthors, Jack and Brian, for keeping up the tradition with their new insights. As ever, my long-time editor, Gary Jansen, has been an invaluable partner. Nothing is more critical than the support given by the entire publishing team, and I extend the warmest gratitude to Diana Baroni and everyone at Harmony Books.

## Jack Tuszynski

I wish to thank my wife, Ela, and my son, Alex, whose unwavering love, support, and inspiration have been instrumental in enabling me to pursue this project despite numerous other commitments. Their presence in my life has provided the motivation and encouragement needed to undertake this endeavor.

I am deeply thankful for the many fruitful scientific interactions and spirited discussions I have had on the subjects of quantum physics and consciousness. I am particularly grateful to Stuart Hameroff, Roger Penrose, Marco Cavaglia, Marco Deriu, Donald Mender, Mark Rasenick, Ursula Werneke, Lloyd Demetrius, Bruce Maciver, and, last but not least, the late great Massimo Cocchi and Kary Mullis. Their insights and contributions have greatly enriched my understanding and shaped the direction of my work.

Furthermore, I owe a significant debt of gratitude to my students, especially Aarat Kalra, Travis Craddock, and Eric Zizzi. Their contagious enthusiasm and remarkable dedication have been a source of inspiration. Their hard work and commitment have contributed immensely to the progress of this project.

## Brian Fertig

I would like to express my deepest appreciation to my wife, Eileen, and son, Matthew, for their unwavering love, strength, and courage. Their support has been instrumental in my pursuit of understanding the fundamental aspects of biological systems, ranging from the most basic to the quantum level, encompassing consciousness, health, friendships, society, and the shared universe.

I owe profound gratitude to Jack Tuszynski and Deepak Chopra, for their invaluable creative insights, which have greatly influenced my journey. I would also like to extend my heartfelt thanks to all those who played a role in guiding the creation of the *Metabolism and Medicine* tome, as well as the inspiring luminaries who generously endorsed my work, thereby contributing to its credibility. I am forever indebted to the late Bruce McEwen, for his shared wisdom and insights.

I am grateful for the engaging conversations I have had with Carol Ash and David O'Hara, as well as the insightful discussions in the doctors' lounge with Vasilios Velmahos, which have been both enriching and inspiring. I take immense pride in Nicolas Velmahos, who has chosen to pursue a career aligned with these interests. I would like to extend my thanks to Amie Thornton and Bob Garrett, for recognizing the value of my contributions.

I wish to acknowledge Vincent Sferra and Michael Whalen, for their thoughtful feedback on numerous ideas, which have been instrumental in shaping my work. Last, I am grateful for the unwavering support and understanding I have received from my medical colleagues, office staff, patients, and my associate, Hassan Kanj. Their encouragement has been invaluable on this journey of exploration and discovery.

# Index